Model-Making for Physicists

Model-Making

for Physicists

by A. D. Bulman

ILLUSTRATED

Thomas Y. Crowell Company

New York

First published in
the United States of America in 1968
Originally published in Great Britain under
the title Model Making for Young Physicists

Designed by
Wladislav Finne
Manufactured in the United States of America
L. C. Card 68–17077
2 3 4 5 6 7 8 9 10

Contents

Part Two. Sound Mechanics, Oscillations

Part Three. Magnetism, Electricity

Model-Making for Physicists

Tools and Techniques

Clever experimenters can achieve a very high standard of workmanship with a surprisingly small number of tools, while others with an enormous range of tools produce only amateurish results. It is therefore impossible to say that certain tools form a minimum equipment. In any case, the experimenter will probably acquire his equipment stage by stage and need not be deterred from starting a project because of some particular lack. As a rough basis, aim at acquiring the following:

Metal-Working Tools

Vise
Hack saw
Hammer
Screwdrivers
Pliers—flat and round-nose
Cutting nippers
Electric or other soldering iron
Electric power drill and lathe attachments

Drills
Taps and dies
Various files
Scriber

Common Wood-Working Tools

Chisels
Common saw
Rip saw
Steel plane
Modern rasp or rasp plane
Brace and bits
A variety of glues and cements
Paints in various colors

The Scrap Box

This vital item will be found to expand rapidly as work proceeds and will contain metal remnants, sheet tin, brass, copper, and aluminum in the form of strip, rods, wires, and tubes, as well as glass, rubber, and the very useful plastics.

Smaller boxes or glass jars will house assortments of screws, washers, nuts and bolts, springs, etc.

Certain processes occur fairly frequently in making apparatus and it may be helpful to clarify these in a general way before dealing with specific models.

First of all, consider the vise. This will form a third hand in the operations of sawing and drilling both wood and metal. Do not spoil the appearance of the work by heavy-handed clamping of the rough metal jaws. Use thick cardboard or other suitable material for cover pieces on the steel jaws. These protectors are easily constructed and may be slipped on or off as required.

A hack saw should not be used so vigorously that the blade becomes unduly hot. Take long, steady strokes in sawing and wet or lubricate the blade from time to time. This last advice also applies to drills, and of course oil must be used with taps and dies. A blunt drill rapidly heats up and it is easy to take the temper out of a steel drill by careless use. Drills should be sharpened at the correct angle by means of a small whetstone.

Always try to use the correct width and shape of screwdriver to suit the screw. The tip of the blade should be ground square to the length and with a small taper (Fig. 1*a*). The very amateurish handyman can be identified at once by the rounded end of his only screwdriver. His chisels have serrated edges, his cutting nippers do not cut, and the pliers he hands out when asked for cutting nippers require Herculean strength to open because of the rust. Incidentally, it is a pity to indent the edge of nippers by attempting to cut very hard steel wire. File a notch and snap it.

Tools in frequent use do not require rust-proofing, but those less often used should be protected with grease, their hinges oiled and kept free from dampness if possible. Naturally, chisels and plane blades require special care to maintain a keen cutting edge.

The soldering bolt should be cleaned with a file and tinned from time to time, since the copper bit tends to become burned and black with oxide.

Soldering should present little difficulty as long as the work surfaces are really clean. If the solder is not ready-fluxed, a suitable flux must be spread on the cleaned metal if the solder is to flow and make a sound joint. The

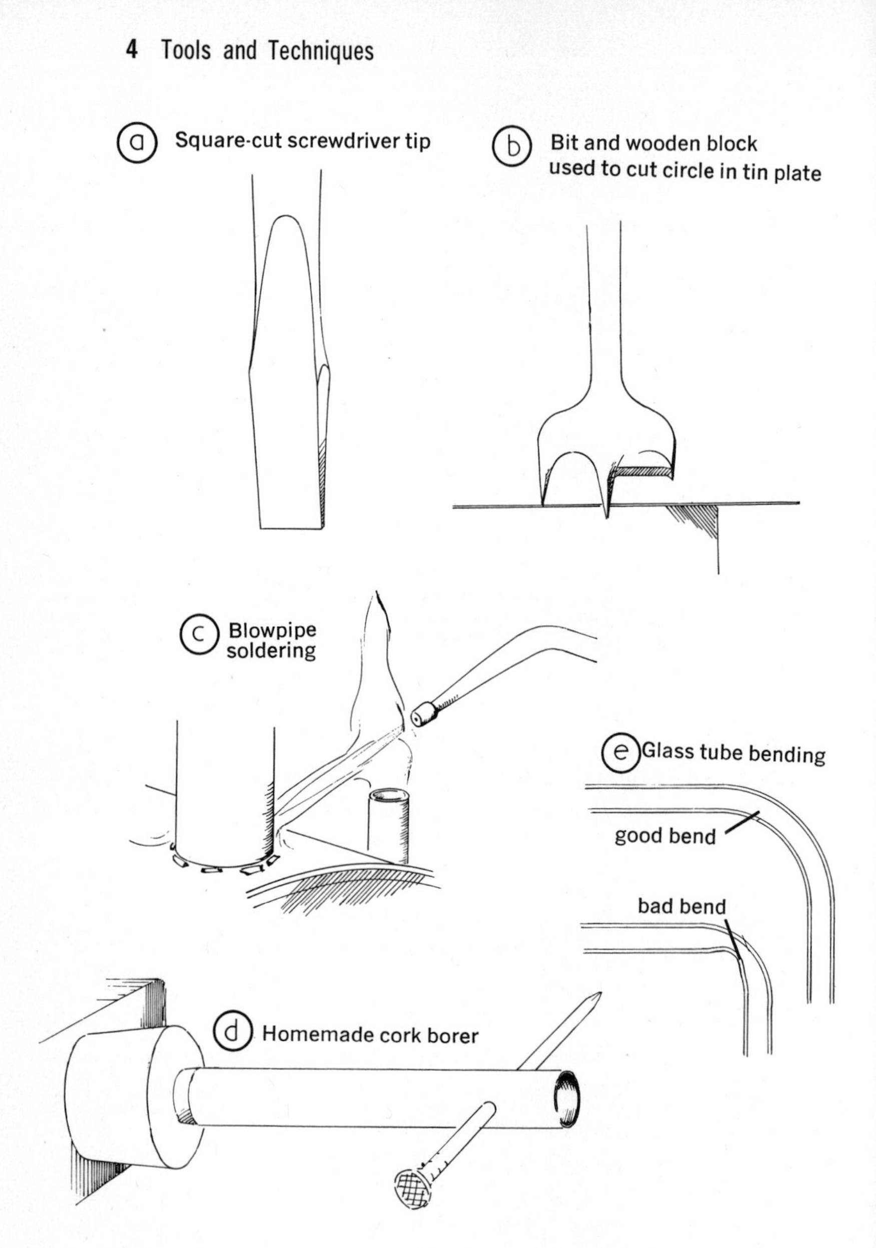
a Square-cut screwdriver tip
b Bit and wooden block used to cut circle in tin plate
c Blowpipe soldering
e Glass tube bending
good bend
bad bend
d Homemade cork borer

Fig. 1

flux helps to prevent the film of oxide which would otherwise form on the surfaces. Bear in mind that solder runs to the hottest part, and this should therefore be the actual jointing surface. If a large object is to be soldered, the whole thing will probably have to be heated or it may conduct away heat too rapidly from the joint itself.

Let us suppose that a wide tube has to be soldered into a piece of tin. First the hole should be cut, slightly undersized. A bit may be used in the brace (Fig. 1*b*) to cut a large hole, but often the simplest way to do this is to drill a ring of holes; then punch out the circle of tin. Finally, smooth the edge with a file and force in the tube. After using emery paper and flux, place clippings of solder around the joint. Hold the surface horizontally and heat it with a small blue Bunsen flame until suddenly the solder runs like quicksilver around the joint. If you have a blowpipe this may be used in conjunction with a soft Bunsen flame to direct heat onto the junction (Fig. 1*c*). Avoid an excess of solder, but further trimming with a soldering bolt may be needed if the seal is imperfect at any point. The smoothest finish will be obtained with the flame alone.

Shapes other than circular are usually chiseled through tinplate by resting it on soft wood and using an old chisel. Boundary forms should be cut out with old scissors, shears, or proper "snips," according to the gauge of metal.

Cork-borers are made in sets of fitting brass tubes of successive sizes; but if only one size is required a cutter may be improvised by sharpening the outer edge of a suitable thin metal tube with a file. A cross hole is drilled, and a rod or a large nail slipped through this serves to turn the borer (Fig. 1*d*). Rest the cork against the vertical edge of the bench. Center the cutter, and while twisting it with the right hand allow the cork, held in the left hand, to slip a quarter turn after each twist of the cutter. Looking down on the borer, check for perpendicularity to the bench edge; the hole should then be straight and central. Start from both ends of the cork to prevent a ragged exit and wet the borer in use. A clean hole will be obtained only with a really sharp-edged borer, and a little practice is needed to produce perfect results.

The different properties of metals soon become apparent to the experimenter. For example, some become more, and some less, springy through hammering. Brass with a high zinc content is very brittle. No brass will stand repeated bending, whereas aluminum and copper will. Cast iron cannot be bent at all. Metals like lead and aluminum will stick to and tend to clog drills and files.

Steel is so common that one should know how to alter its properties. Use a piece of clock spring for practice. Heat it to redness and cool it slowly. It will have become soft and malleable (and oxidized) and can then be filed or drilled with ease. Again heat it to redness, then chill it suddenly in cold water. It is brittle, and snaps rather than bends. At this stage clean the surface with emery cloth and gently reheat it. The metal undergoes a fascinating series of changes in its properties, losing hardness and gaining, then losing, elasticity; and the process may be stopped at any stage by quenching the metal in cold water. Furthermore, the oxide film covering the metal indicates by its color the stage reached. Spring elasticity is denoted by the change from straw color to dark blue. This process of diminishing the hardness of steel is called tempering it.

It is useful to be able to make spiral springs and this is not at all difficult. Clamp in the vise a rod, such as a nail, smaller in diameter than the required spring. Together with the nail, clamp one end of a length of piano wire, and holding the wire in a cloth wrap it tightly and evenly around the rod. A preliminary trial will quickly show the thickness of rod and wire and the number of turns needed for a spring of particular strength and diameter.

Glassworking is, of course, a specialized art requiring training and much practice, but you should be conversant with one or two primary points in dealing with glass tubing. When the length of tube has been decided upon, scratch a mark at that point with a triangular file. Press the file hard and move it slowly, but do not file away at the glass or you will simply destroy the edge of the file. With thumbs near the mark and pointing away from the body, sharply twist the wrists inward and the glass should break cleanly at right angles to the length. Soften the sharp edges in the side of a hot Bunsen flame in order to round them off.

In bending glass tubing the aim should be to form a perfectly smooth curve. The tube should have uniform thickness around the curve and not show any inward kink at a sharp bend (Fig. 1*e*). Soften a good length of the glass, twirling it in the Bunsen flame, until the stage is reached when it colors the flame yellow. It is then near its melting point. Take the glass out of the flame; bend it slowly. The glass may be reheated and bent in stages if necessary. Let it cool down very slowly in a soft and diminishing yellow flame in order to anneal the glass. This obviates strains, which could cause fracture later.

It is not difficult to cut wide glass tubing by scratching right around it with a file or an ordinary glass-cutter and then leading a crack around this mark by touching the tube with a red-hot glass rod, but this requires a little practice.

In the past, cabinetmakers relied on the glue pot and

the messy boiling-up of fish glue for jointing, but nowadays the business of bonding materials has been enormously simplified by the great variety of boxed and tubed cements put on the market.

The experimenter will soon collect several varieties suited to different materials and conditions. Waterproof epoxy resin adhesives are easy to use. The resin powders are made into a paste and spread on one surface. The adjoining surface is treated with an acidic solution, and when set the final bond is of great strength and is waterproof.

Epoxy is ideal for adhesion to plastics, but the more flexible, heat-resistant liquid solder is needed for rubbery or fabric surfaces. When ordinary soldering is not feasible, use cold solder, which is also electrically insulating.

The only guide needed here is to use the right cement to stand up to the conditions of strain, dampness, and heat to which the joint will eventually be subject.

One striking feature of modern engineering and electrical laboratories is the amount of bright color used, and this is not designed solely to catch the eye of the visitor. Steam, compressed air, water, A.C. and D.C. lines, and so on, are recognized by their brightly painted conduits. Most laboratories also carry this coloring on to bench terminals and electrical meter terminals. This not only makes for fewer mistakes, but it brightens the surroundings.

If a scientific model is worth making it is probably worth finishing off with paint in an attractive way.

On opening a can of paint it is advisable to smell it and find out the particular medium or solvent used in it. One should not then make any error in using the wrong thinner. Turpentine may usually be safely added to oil paints, while acetone or amyl acetate are solvents for the cellulose types. Note that the two types do not mix. Oil paints and oil varnish are slower in drying than their cellulose counterparts. A cellulose paint, if laid over an oil paint, will lift it off, producing an unpleasant mess, though oils may sometimes be overlaid on cellulose. The beauty of cellulose lies in its gloss and in the speed of drying, but do not forget that the solvents are highly flammable.

Shellac in alcohol is serviceable as a quick-drying varnish. It may be used on metal as well as wood, but no thinner other than denatured alcohol should be added to it.

Before beginning any experiment, read it through carefully until you understand completely the principles involved, and have assembled all the materials you will need for the model you are about to build. There is nothing so frustrating as having to stop or spoil an experiment halfway through because you don't have the proper materials or have not understood a procedure thoroughly.

Some Sensible Precautions

The use of power supplies and of tools involves some element of danger, and there are inherent risks in experimental work, so that a word of caution may not be out of place. We are told that more than 28,000 people die from accidents in the home in the United States each year and it would be sad indeed if this book were the cause of even one more. Common-sense care is the answer.

In the following pages instructions are given for making and using electrical apparatus, and this often implies use of house current. It requires special care to avoid shock, since wet hands can easily result in a fatal current passing through the body. This is an ever present danger, which electrical engineers and radio and television men recognize and treat with respect—familiarity is not allowed to breed contempt. This is a case where the risks are too great for any carelessness. If possible, a knowledgeable adult should supervise any work with house current. A suitably insulated transformer giving low voltage, as for toy trains, may often be substituted for the 110 volts supplied to houses.

We know that electrical devices are in use every day in millions of homes—toasters, irons, vacuum cleaners, power tools, and so on—and the actual percentage of accidents is small, but even this might be reduced with a little forethought.

In manipulation of radio and television, bare wires will be unavoidable. *Always* pull out the plug before tampering with wiring, and double-check any change that has been made before reconnecting. Wet hands and cement floors, especially wet floors, are a great danger in electrical work. Remember that it is not high voltage which is dangerous in itself; it is the large current which results through low resistance. The body, largely blood and salty fluids, has low resistance, and if current is led in through damp surfaces the effect may be lethal. Faulty wiring, abraded insulation, and bare ends are the usual causes of accidents with electric tools, lamp extensions, and so on. Be warned and check these points with particular care. *Never* touch possibly live wiring or equipment and water pipes, taps, bathtubs, or cisterns simultaneously, and take special care with temporary extensions to lamps and drills.

Should you ever be in the predicament of finding a person unconscious through shock, turn off the switch or disconnect the power quickly. Then, using *dry* wood or *dry* clothing, push or pull the victim away from the wire.

Every household should have a readily accessible first-aid cabinet containing essential items such as gauze bandages, adhesive tape, and scissors. One would be fortunate if in carrying out all the mechanical processes and experiments described in this book one sustained no minor burn or cut. Cold water may be run over a small burn to reduce pain. If the skin is not blistered, smooth on petroleum jelly, then cover with sterile dressings. But if the skin is blistered use the coverings alone to exclude air, and do not apply oil or ointment. Do not break or drain the blisters. Of course, if burns or scalds are at all extensive a doctor should be called.

The greatest care must be exercised in using chemicals, especially the very corrosive battery fluids. A small splash of sulphuric acid or of caustic potash in the eye is painful and very dangerous. The treatment for this is immediate sluicing with plenty of water or saline solution, one teaspoonful of salt to one pint of previously boiled water. Cover the eye and consult a doctor at once.

Dealing with cuts calls for scrupulous cleanliness. Wash hands thoroughly with soap and running water, then use a mild antiseptic on sterile gauze. When hands are dry, bandage the wound. Watch for signs of infection in the region around it for a few days and if necessary see a doctor. The possibility of injuring oneself using carpentry and metal-work tools is small if they are being used correctly. In particular, never drive a chisel *toward* the hand holding the work, and if a screw is being inserted, never hold the work so that the screwdriver can slip upward toward the face or into the eye.

The eyes are far too precious to take risks with, and when necessary they must be safeguarded. If lead is to be cast in sand or other molding material, this must be dry to avoid spurting of the molten metal. It is suggested that a simple visor be made. This may be a thin, clear piece of plastic attached by elastic and worn in front of the eyes when doing work which involves risk, such as melting lead, using grinders, pouring acids, and so on.

No experimenter can entirely escape the odd cut and burn—perhaps even salutary to the beginner—but after these warnings the author must disclaim any responsibility for accident caused by lack of common-sense care.

Part one

Heat, Light, Color

1
A Bunsen Burner

A Bunsen burner is used so frequently in science that it is difficult to envisage operations without it, although for some purposes an old-fashioned alcohol lamp will suffice. Alcohol gives a nice clean flame for soldering.

The Bunsen burner utilizes a fine jet of gas which passes adjustable air holes and pulls a supply of air into its stream. This is the same principle on which carburetors pull air into the vaporized gasoline before suction of the explosive mixture into the cylinders of a car.

The physicist's requirement is usually a clean hot flame, and a Bunsen burner will produce a roaring, intense one when needed. It is rarely used with the air holes closed, as the pure gas burns with a yellow, smoky flame, but the halfway stage, the soft blue flame, is very useful for boiling, soft-soldering, and so on.

If you do not already own a Bunsen burner, it is a simple and instructive exercise to make one up from scrap. There are no precise requirements for the size of the Bunsen burner; the materials to make it can depend on what your scrap box contains. The brass tubes used

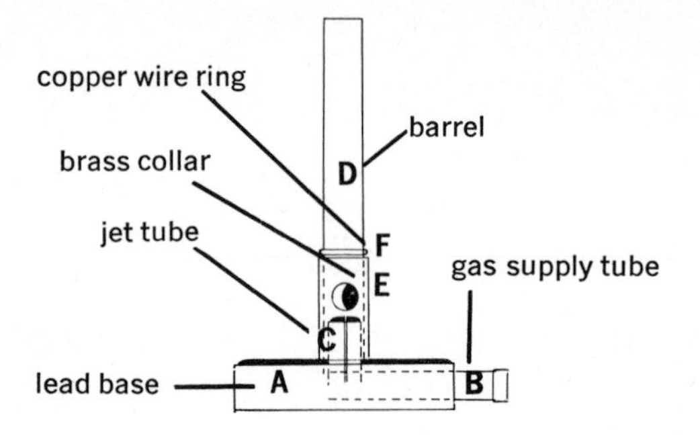

Fig. 2 The Bunsen burner

here were about ⅜ in. in diameter, but if you already have brass tubing of different dimensions, go ahead and improvise. That principle may be adopted for any item in this book.

Pieces of scrap lead are melted on a kitchen gas range in a strong tin box or discarded pot, then poured into a shoe-polish can. This casting (the can may be left on) forms a heavy base, *A*, Fig. 2, for the burner. With a brace and bit, holes are drilled vertically and horizontally as shown to take the brass tubes *B* and *C*. These must be slightly tapered and hammered into the lead. The gas supply tube *B* should extend about ¾ in. into the base, but the jet tube *C* must just enter the horizontal hole. When the tube *C* has been tested for size, it is filled with a lead plug, cast in the tube. The lead is poured in around a centrally placed greasy sewing needle which, when extracted, leaves the jet hole. During the casting, the tube may be held in a shallow hole drilled in a wooden block with the needle precisely centered in the tube.

Suitable diameter brass tubes are needed for the barrel *D* and the brass collar *E* in which matching air holes are to be cut. If the collar presents difficulty a tin tube may be substituted but will not look so well. If *D* is not already a good fit on the tube *C* it may be sealed in position with epoxy glue. The easiest way to make the matching air holes in *D* and *E* is first to run the tubes onto tapered dowel rods held in a vise. Flatten the tubes somewhat with a file, then use a ¼-in. drill. Finally, trim the holes to shape with a round file, again using it to smooth the inner surface of the collar so that it turns easily on *D*. A ring of copper wire, *F*, is soldered onto *D* just above the collar, thereby preventing loss of the air adjuster.

With double air holes, i.e., drilled right through the tubes, it may be possible to overdo the air supply. In this case the burner may "strike back" in use. It should not be allowed to burn for long at the lead jet or this may soften and close up the hole.

Finally, a coat of gray paint on the base will enhance the Bunsen burner's appearance, and polished brass is better preserved when it has been varnished. For this purpose dissolve a little shellac in denatured alcohol and apply rapidly with a soft brush while the tubes are revolving. A milky appearance is avoided by warming the work to be lacquered.

2
Thermoscopes

These experiments are concerned with the expansion of fluids with heat, and for them you will need a piece of thin glass tubing 2 ft. long with a $\frac{1}{10}$-in. bore.

Bore the bottle's cork to take the tubing as a tight fit. If found to leak it will have to be waxed (Fig. 3). Color some water in the bottom of the bottle with red ink and insert the tube to nearly touch the bottom. Now, by blowing in a bubble or two, we can cause the water to rise to a convenient height low in the tube. If it remains there it can be assumed that no leakage is occurring at the cork.

This arrangement, known as an air thermoscope, with the addition of a suitable scale on the stem can be used as a rough form of thermometer. It is, however, extremely sensitive to temperature change.

The heat of the hands placed around the bottle will cause a considerable rise in the water level in the tube because of the great expansibility of the air trapped in the bottle. The expansion is, in fact, $\frac{1}{273}$ of the volume of air at 0°C for each 1°C rise. On the other hand, the apparatus is far from accurate as a permanent form of thermometer because, being open to the air, it is subject to barometric as well as temperature change. Also, the liquid will gradually evaporate.

Plunging the bottle into a basin of hot water will cause a rapid expansion of the air, which will eject a stream of colored water from the top of the tube.

Now, as a second experiment, make a "water thermoscope" from the same apparatus (Fig. 3) by filling it completely with colored water. In this case the glass tubing may end just below the cork. Any change in level

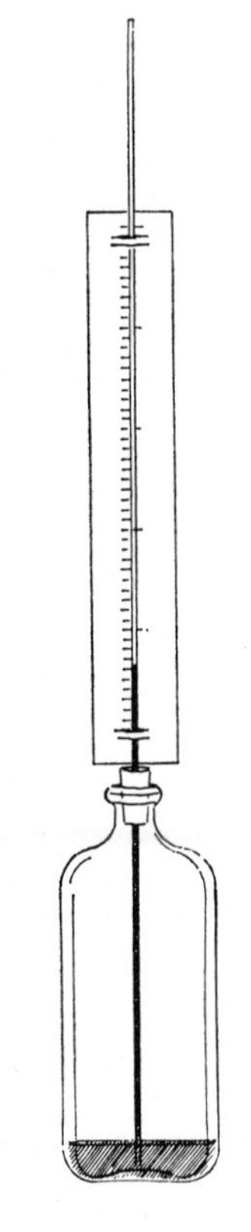

Fig. 3 The air thermoscope

will now result from the difference in expansion of the water and the glass bottle. Plunge the thermoscope into a basin of hot water and carefully observe the meniscus of the water in the tube. It first drops appreciably. This is caused by the expansion of the glass increasing the internal volume of the bottle. Next it begins to rise slowly, passes its original starting point on the scale, and continues to rise until the water in the bottle has acquired the same temperature as that in the basin. Although water has a vastly smaller expansion than the air of the first experiment, it is large enough to be measured quite easily with this apparatus.

The so-called coefficient of volume expansion is simply the fractional increase of the volume at 0°C for each 1°C rise of temperature. This, of course, has different values for different liquids.

3
A Simple Heat Engine

The conversion of heat into more obvious forms of motion has been the concern of engineers since the earliest times. The steam approach has certainly been exploited to the full from the time of Watt to the designers of the modern steam turbine. The atomic generating stations still depend upon it. The efficiency of steam may therefore blind us to a simpler energy conversion by direct expansion of air.

Air expands with rise of temperature or, if it is not allowed to expand, its pressure increases proportionately. The former fact is precisely stated in Charles's Law: "Under constant pressure the volume of the gas varies directly with the absolute temperature," and in the Pressure Law: "At constant volume the pressure varies directly with the temperature."

The following paragraphs describe the construction of a simple form of hot-air engine. The model will never develop any appreciable power, but it well illustrates the direct conversion of heat energy into mechanical energy.

Air is alternately heated and cooled by being pushed to and fro by a loose displacer between the hot and cold ends of a cylinder. Part of the heat supplied therefore does work in expanding the air against the resistance of a well-fitting piston in the power cylinder. This mechanical energy is now imparted to the flywheel and the loose displacer piston is moved up and down by the cranked shaft of this flywheel. The same air, if we assume no leakages from the cylinders, is acting as the working substance throughout. Notice that it is obeying neither the special condition stipulated in the Pressure Law (the volume is not constant) nor that of Charles's Law (the pressure is not constant) but is combining the two effects in a very interesting manner.

Prior to attempting this model, it is a good idea to collect an assortment of different sizes of empty cans from canned fruit, etc., as a selection is needed. Also in this and other models it will be found that plumbers' scrap, such as pieces of brass and copper pipe, will prove to be extremely useful.

This model is a good exercise in soldering technique, as several soft-soldered parts are closely adjacent and the joints must be airtight. The novice at soldering should observe two points. First, the surfaces must be scraped really clean and preferably given a preliminary tinning with the flux-cored solder. Second, the parts to be joined should be held rigidly in position, by wiring or otherwise, while the soldering is carried out. For a body of large heat capacity or big cooling surface the Bunsen may be used direct, but for smaller joints use a blowpipe or the electric soldering iron.

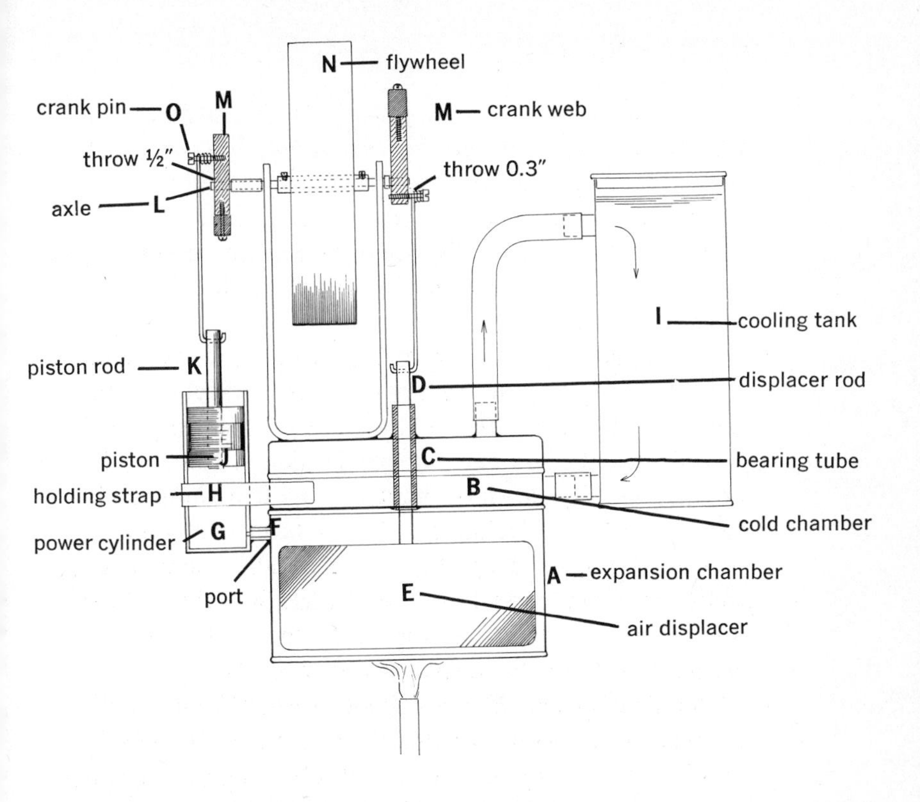

Fig. 4 A simple heat engine

The parts to obtain first, since they will probably be the most difficult to get, are the power cylinder *G* and piston *J* (Fig. 4), then the rod *D* carrying the displacer, together with the bearing tube *C* into which *D* fits. For the power cylinder, a smooth brass or copper tube about ½ in. in diameter and 2 in. long, closed at the bottom, is suitable. The piston should be a really good sliding fit in this; if a metal one is not possible, one could be improvised by turning hardwood, such as seasoned box-wood or ebony. Other possibilities for the piston are casting it in light alloy in the cylinder itself, or using two coins mounted on a central rod. One method of ensuring a good fit that has proved successful is to turn a shallow groove around a boxwood piston, fill this with a cold metal solder and while still soft push it into the previously greased cylinder, allowing it to set there. Except in small models, however, wood is not really a suitable piston material because of its distortion with moisture content. Mount the piston rod *K* in the center of the piston as shown in Fig. 4.

The expansion chamber *A* is a cylindrical can, 4 in. in diameter by 2¾ in. high, in which the displacer will move up and down. The bottom of this is to be heated over a small Bunsen flame or alcohol lamp, while at the top the box is sealed by another can containing cold water *B*. This cold chamber *B* can be a can 4 in. in diameter by 1 in. deep. Pipe tobacco and some fancy candy come in cans this size. Carefully drill a hole through the center of the top of *B*, then solder in the bearing tube *C* for the displacer rod *D*.

The air displacer *E* is a cylinder turned from a light seasoned wood such as balsa. It is to be ⅛ in. less in radius than the box *A*, and about 2 in. high so it can freely move up and down ¾ in., thereby transferring the air from the high- to the low-temperature end of the box and causing alternate expansion and contraction. A disk of tin on the underside would equalize the heat there, reducing the possibility of the wood burning. The displacer rod *D* should be mounted perpendicular and precisely in the center of *B*, and since the whole unit is to be as light in weight as possible, a closed tube is preferable to a rod here.

It must be remembered that the interior will be inaccessible later when the displacer is inserted in *A*, and the cooling tin *B* is soldered onto the top of *A*. This would then be airtight but for the ⅛-in. hole *F*, which is the port to the power cylinder *G*.

A short brass tube at *F* links the tin *A* and the power cylinder *G*. The cylinder and tube are correctly positioned and wired together while a holding strap *H* (which will prevent the power cylinder from wobbling) and the short tube at *F* are soldered into position. The hole *F* should be well up the side of the box, near the cold tank, so the soldering will not be affected by heating of the base of the can during operation. Because of the heat, a trace of air leakage may possibly develop around the base of the can, which is just pressed on in the factory sealing process, but this should not be great enough to prevent the engine working well: the rate of pressure fluctuation prevents any serious loss either here or at the displacer rod.

The volume of water in *B* alone is too small to remain cool for any considerable time and a cooling tank *I* must therefore be added at the side. This may be a large can attached by soldered ½-in. metal tubes or connected with a few inches of detachable hose pipe. In any case it should allow free circulation of the cooling water. When heated at the under face of *B*, a convection current is initiated in this water and the large volume and area of *I* maintain a low temperature for a reasonable time. *I* should be painted matte black.

The three modes of transfer of heat from the air in *A* are:

i. Conduction through the base of tin *B*.
ii. Convection by circulation of water between *B* and *I*.
iii. Radiation loss from the extensive black surface of *I*.

Construct the U-shaped support for the flywheel out of strong metal wire. Solder the bottom of the U to the

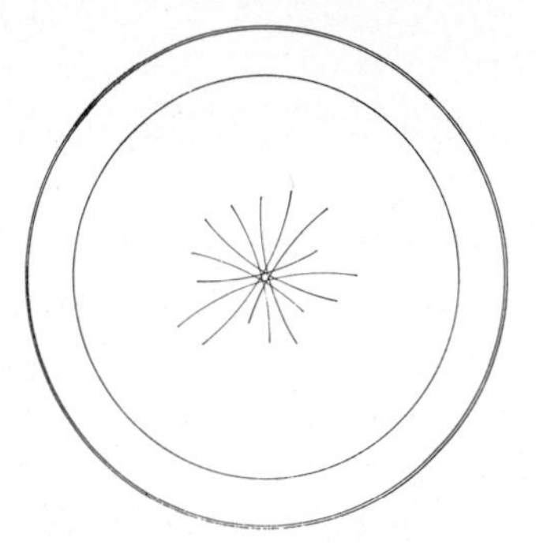

Fig. 5 Finding center of the flywheel can with dividers

cold chamber and make loops at the ends for the axle to pass through. Pieces of the electrical barrel connector may be used as collars to separate the crank webs from the legs of the support.

A satisfactory flywheel can easily be made from a small tobacco can or candy container with an accurately centered hole. This is done with divider marks described from the rim of the base and lid, as in Fig. 5. The center is then punched through with an awl before being enlarged with a reamer; a twist drill may tear the hole off-center in thin metal. Added mass is given to the rim by a strip of lead, or lead-covered cable, stuck around the inside of the rim with glue. A brass tube with 2 insert screws, such as an electrical barrel-connector, is soldered through the middle of the flywheel. By means of it the wheel may be clamped in correct position on its axle. A good axle may be made from a steel knitting needle. Build the crank webs of ¼-in. Masonite. They should be about the same size as shown in Fig. 6.

Three holes *P*, *Q*, and *R* are drilled through the sector-shaped Masonite, the distance *PQ* being the required throw and the holes being the requisite size for a tight fit on the crankpin and the axle. A slot is sawed down to *R;* then a clamping bolt is screwed through a cross hole

S. The length *PQ*, in the case of the displacer crank (about 0.3 in.), is half the total available travel of the displacer without touching top or bottom. In the case of the piston crank, it is about ½ in., half the total stroke of the piston between the top of its cylinder and the lowest point above the port.

Screwed to the opposite end of the crank web is a lead weight *T*, which just counterbalances the weight of the displacer or the piston, as the case may be. This weight is separately determined for each, other attachments to the shaft having been removed. These detachable crank webs make for ease in adjusting, setting, and, of course, dismantling the engine. A balanced design is obtained by mounting the flywheel between the bearings, with the two cranks outside. Use bicycle spokes or sturdy wire to attach the crankpins to the piston and displacer rod.

A fair degree of latitude in dimensions may be allowed in this model, but one restriction should be observed. The displacer should nearly touch the sides and also, at the ends of its stroke, the bottom and top of the expansion chamber. Otherwise, the dead space forms a volume of unworked air taking up and cushioning the pressure fluctuation vitally needed in the cylinder itself. For the same reason, if the displacer is replaced by a box (for lightness) it must be a completely sealed one.

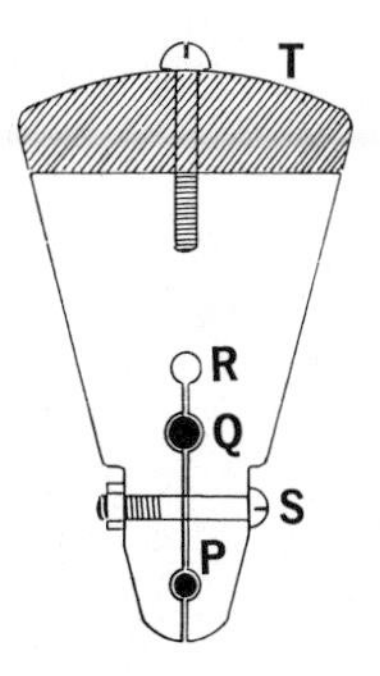

Fig. 6 Crank web

The relative position of the cranks, about 90°, is clearly of great importance in efficient running. After construction the whole machine should be oiled and checked for free running. The two cranks should be set at right angles, and with a small blue flame placed under the box the engine should start to revolve almost at once. Working with a fixed-size flame, we may estimate the speed of the engine. Appropriate small adjustments of the phase angle between the two cranks can then be made to give the greatest rate of revolution.

4
Hygrometers

A hygroscope "indicates" and a hygrometer "measures" the state of moisture content of the atmosphere. Some simple devices which indicate humidity by color change of chemical salts are clearly in the hygroscope class, while instruments using paper, hair, or cellophane may be made accurate enough to be regarded as hygrometers. There are many forms of apparatus from which relative humidity may be determined (including various "dew-point" instruments) ranging from the simple wet and dry bulb thermometer to the sling psychrometers of the meteorologists.

The type we propose to describe here is dependent on the fact that the length of a paper strip changes with its moisture content. An annoyance to the watercolorist is the wrinkling of his paper when it becomes wet, but here we shall be exploiting the phenomenon usefully. The instrument is simply made (see Fig. 7) and reasonably accurate, but care and some degree of neat-fingered skill is required to produce a pleasing specimen.

First obtain a thin strip of springy metal foil such as a

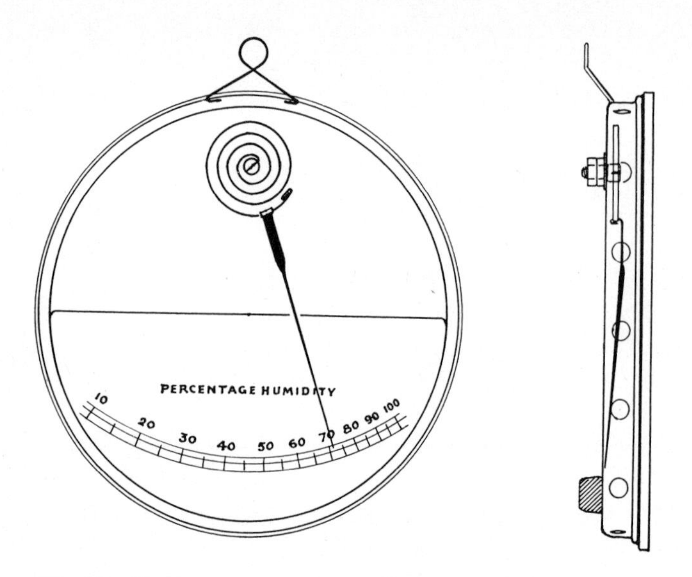

Fig. 7 Hygrometer—paper and foil type

scrap of brass weather stripping. The springy brass tape which rewinds a spring tape measure would do if a discarded one is available. Roughen one side of this foil, a strip 6 in. or more long by ½ in. wide, with emery cloth or sandpaper and then coat it with Duco cement. Cut a similar-sized strip of good quality paper, such as thin watercolor paper or vellum, and attach it with the same cement, allowing it to dry thoroughly. Rule lines lengthwise on the paper about 1 mm apart and with sharp scissors cut off some strips of this width. The dual strip should adhere well and not separate in the process. After wetting the paper side of such a strip make it into a neat, close spiral by drawing the metal side over a sharp angle or otherwise coil it. The coil should have the paper side out.

This is all the mechanism. The metal maintains its length as the humidity changes but the paper expands and contracts, causing slight coiling or uncoiling of the spiral, to which a light pointer is cemented. For the casing the lid of a paint can, 4 in. in diameter, is very suitable. Drill a hole ½ in. from one side to take a small bolt with a soft washer and lock nuts. The inside coil of the spiral is glued into the slot of the screw head and a light pointer, which may be cut from the same foil, is glued radially to an outer coil. Turning the bolt allows for setting the pointer.

The actual number of coils will depend on the strength of the spring metal—if weak enough, one or two turns is enough, but five coils may be necessary to give a pointer traverse of about 10 cm around a scale of 7-cm radius. Probably a variety of sizes of paper-foil spirals should be made at the same time and the most effective length and width of strip may be selected.

The whole instrument is likely to be on a larger scale than the neat commercial hygrometers and of course in its present state it is just a hygro*scope*. Breathing on it should cause a considerable movement of the pointer.

The next stage is the calibration of the scale. Smooth white cardboard should be glued on the back of the case behind the pointer and, from the center of the spiral, arcs should be drawn to take the divisions. Zero humidity is a point easily found by completely drying out the instrument in front of a radiator. Also the 100% mark can readily be located when the paper is actually wet. These fixed points are first marked in pencil. Unfortunately, the range cannot just be subdivided equally to mark the intermediate percentages, because the instrument scaling is not likely to be linear, i.e., proportionate to humidity. This in fact means that the divisions are more and more crowded toward the high-humidity end of the scale.

One way of coping with this problem is to borrow a correctly set commercial model and place it, together with your embryo instrument, in a closed tank. Start with a dish of water in the tank and, after sufficient time for the air to be saturated, check the 100% mark. Then, having removed the water dish, progressively dry out the tank with a dish of dry calcium chloride or phosphorus pentoxide and mark the pointer positions at 90%, 80%, 70%, etc., as recorded on the correct hygrometer. Alternatively one could start with the tank perfectly dry and then by breathing into it obtain the intermediate humidities. The spaces can be divided sufficiently accurately by eye and marked in pencil. The divisions and numbers should finally be drawn carefully in India ink.

Readings are meaningless unless air can freely circulate past the paper, and the side of the casing must therefore be drilled with a number of ventilation holes. A clock glass or other glass plate can be glued to the front of the box.

To avoid rusting and improve the appearance, the pointer and casing may be painted with black paint, and the attachment of a ring enables the instrument to be suspended.

5 Some Optical Illusions

The normal human eye is a miracle of accuracy and sensitivity and is the most precious of the five senses through which we know the outside world. It is nevertheless true that the eye may be induced to play tricks upon our interpretation of physical reality.

We are all very familiar with the sense of continuity afforded by persistence of vision. An illusion of continuous movement is given to separate motion-picture frames and our television-screen picture is a built-up one using moving spots of light. This desirable result stems from what, in a sense, is a defect of our eyes, namely, that perception of the picture on the retina remains for nearly $\frac{1}{12}$ second after the stimulating cause has ceased.

On a sheet of white paper outline a large birdcage about 7 in. deep and 5 in. wide and put a black spot near the middle. Draw on another sheet a 3-in. silhouette of a parrot with a prominent black eye. Fill it in with your most brilliant red paint, or cut out a parrot in bright red paper and paste it in the middle of a sheet of white paper. Now gaze fixedly at the eye of the red parrot while counting up to 60 slowly. Transfer your gaze to the spot in the empty cage and after a second or so a bright green parrot will appear inside the cage. Green is the complementary color of red.

The explanation is as follows. The retina nerves have become less sensitive to the red of the parrot-shaped area during the 60 seconds. Since the white sheet reflects all the wavelengths, the remainder of the spectrum, greenish in effect, is then emphasized on an identical area.

Artists know well that we see selectively, i.e., we see

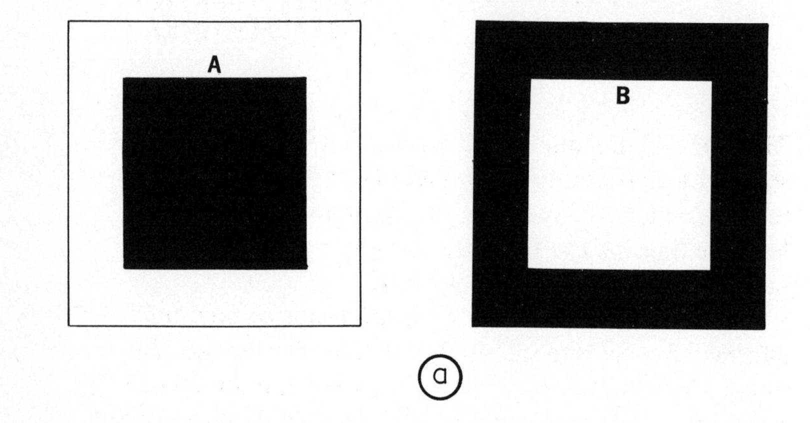

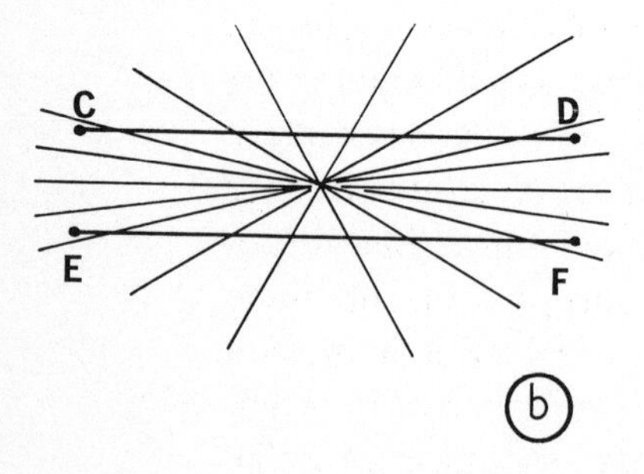

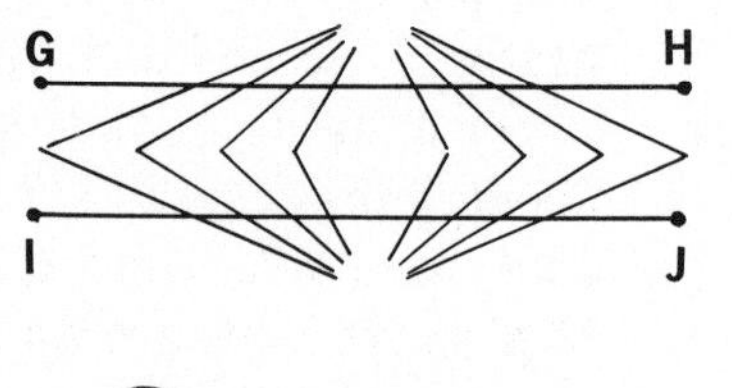

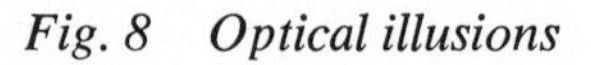
Fig. 8 Optical illusions

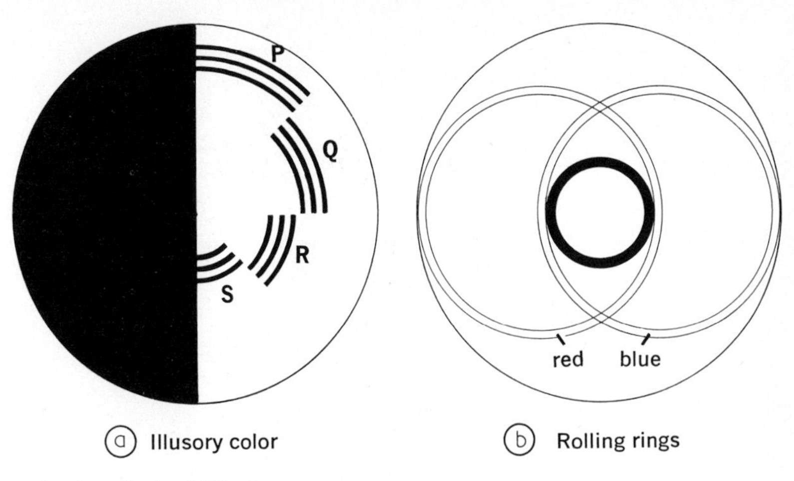

Fig. 9 Optical illusions

what we wish to see. This is achieved not only by the clever focusing mechanism of our eyes but mentally by the unconscious rejection of unwanted elements. That the brain may be tricked into false conclusions may be demonstrated by the following very simple experiments which require little more than some careful drawing. It is best to use a good-quality, thick, white drawing paper, making the diagrams with instruments and India ink.

In Fig. 8*a* two squares, *A* and *B,* of identical size are drawn. Square *A* is blackened while *B* is surrounded by a wide black border. The illusion is that the white area *B* invariably looks larger than an equal-sized black one. Actually a white point gives a circle of stimulation on the retina and hence the white area encroaches on the black area in each case.

Diagrams *b* and *c,* Fig. 8, show apparent distortion caused by overlaid lines. *CD* and *EF* are actually parallel, but with the addition of the radial lines appear "bow-legged." Likewise the parallels *GH* and *IJ* give the impression of being "knock-kneed" as a result of the overlaid diamonds.

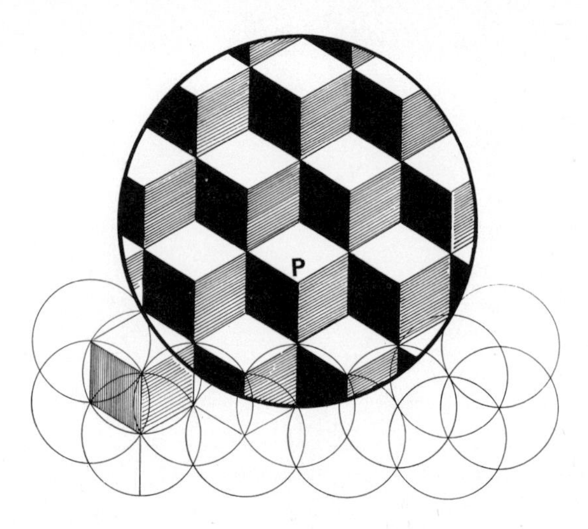

Fig. 10

The diagrams of Fig. 9 are intended to be rotated fairly slowly. This can be done on a phonograph turntable, but it is easy to make up a simple spinner from an Erector set. The disks should be drawn about 1 ft. in diameter in India ink. Disk *a* is known as Benham's top and gives a fascinating color illusion. It should be rotated, not too rapidly, in a clockwise direction and it is seen that the concentric black rings have the appearance of being colored. *P* may look turquoise or bluish, *Q* and *R* tend to green and yellow, while *S* is red. Reversal of the direction of rotation reverses this color sequence, *S* becoming turquoise and *P* red. The apparent coloration may be due to time lapse in stimulation of the brain from the cones of the retina. Exposure to white light reflected from the different rings is different in time, but the full explanation, physiological as well as physical, is still unknown to us.

Fig. 9*b* shows three differently colored bands. Spun at the correct slow speed and in a good light, the outer rings appear to roll around the inner one in an amusing way. Many other revolving-disk illusions are known and described in books on optics.

Fig. 10 illustrates another interesting type of illusion. Draw a set of interlocking circles and, using their intersection points, construct the hexagon pattern indicated outside the large circle. Shade the appropriate diamonds to produce the appearance of cubes in relief. How many whole cubes do you see in the circle?

Confusion in interpretation here arises from the assumed angle of lighting. Most viewers mentally accept top lighting as natural and this makes the corner *P* a projection. Even without inverting the drawing, however, the same point *P* may appear to be an indentation. This would alter the apparent number of complete cubes within the circle from six to seven.

6
Color-Mixing Apparatus

Most people respond to the fascination of the interplay of colored light, as shown by the popularity of such effects in motion pictures.

A simple piece of apparatus can be constructed to illustrate the mixtures resulting from varying proportions of the three primary lights—red, blue, and green. It should be noted at the outset that this is not equivalent to mixing red, blue, and green paints (which in any case the artist does not consider to be his primaries). The artist's colors are merely residual colors reflected to the eye after the pigments have absorbed certain wavelengths from white light, which is a mixture of all the wavelengths. The experiments described here mix the actual lights; these are either seen direct or reflected from a white ground.

The following general visual impressions are obtained:

i. The three primaries together give white if in correctly balanced proportions.

ii. Red and blue give magenta, a purplish or wine-like red.
iii. Blue and green give turquoise or peacock blue.
iv. Green and red give yellow—a somewhat surprising result to the artist, who would anticipate a dirty brown or gray.

The basic requirement here is a group of gelatin filters. These should be "pure" colors—red, blue, and green such as are used in stage projection lights, but a few square inches of each will suffice.

Construct a box of wood or metal according to the plan shown in the black lines of the diagram (Fig. 11). It has three windows, *A*, *B*, and *C*, each 1 in. by 2 in. Fix the three primary filters to cover *A*, *B*, and *C*. Now *D* and *E* are hinged doors faced on the inside with slips of mirror. The latter may be attached to plywood by

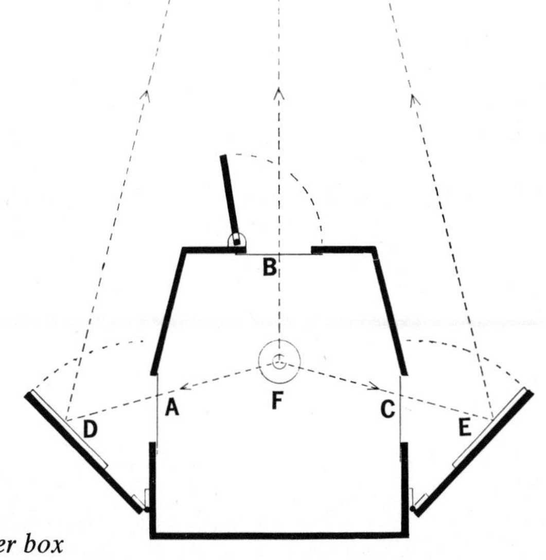

Fig. 11
The color-mixer box

binding the edges with cellophane tape, but do not attempt to use glue on the mirrors or the backing-paint will peel off. *F* is a car headlight bulb, e.g., 36 watt, run from a suitable storage battery or stepdown transformer. You might use a bright tensor lamp.

Any two or all of the colors may be projected onto white paper or the ceiling of a darkened room to produce quite beautiful color combinations. If the secondary filters magenta, turquoise, and yellow are also available, these may be substituted for the primaries in the windows of the light-box, increasing the range of experiment. The effect of overlapping the shadows cast by a rod placed in the beams should also be studied.

A Kaleidoscope

A kaleidoscope is an old-fashioned toy, but a well-made one can be fascinating. Two mirrors set at an angle of 60° to one another show six images, the last two being coincident, of an object between them (see Figs. 12*a* and *b*). In Fig. 12*a* the object represented by the spot *O* between mirrors *AP* and *BP* forms primary images I_1 and I_2 in the two mirrors; then they in turn form secondary images I_3 and I_4. The latter are still in front of the planes of the mirrors and can therefore form two coincident final images I_5 and I_6, but these are then behind both mirrors and cannot form further images. In general, if mirrors lie at some angle $\theta°$ which gives an even value to $360/\theta$ then the number of multiple images seen is $360/\theta - 1$, the -1 resulting from the coincidence mentioned. Thus the object itself and the five images

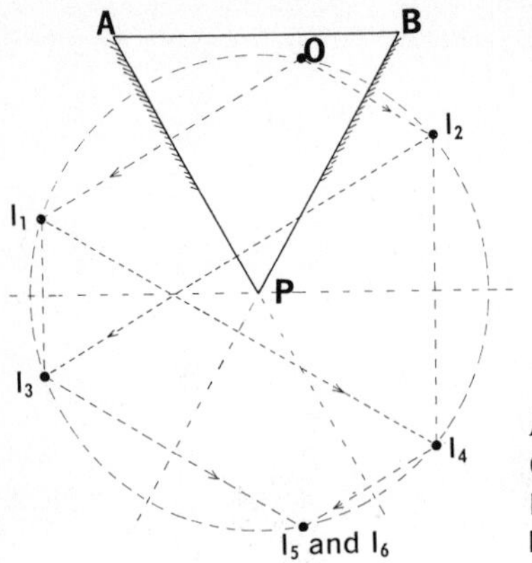

Fig. 12a
O = Object
I_1 etc. = Images
I_5 and I_6 = Coincident last images

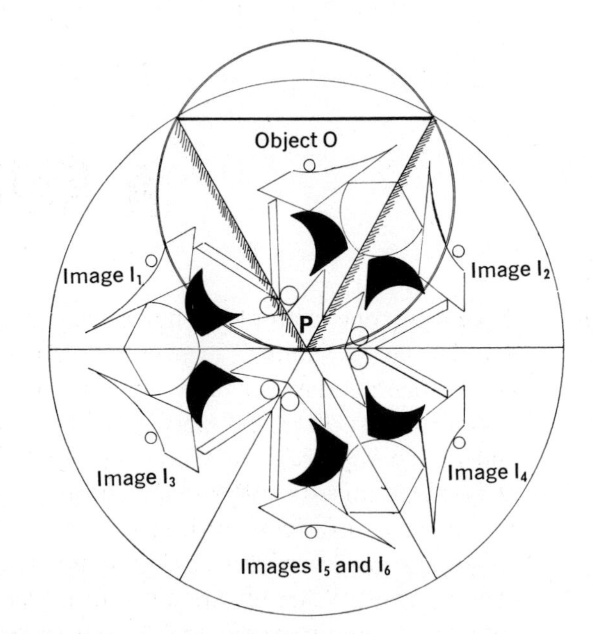

Fig. 12b Multiple images in the kaleidoscope

form a trisymmetrical design, as is evident from Fig. 12*b*. Elementary experiments with mirrors show that the image of each object point lies behind the mirror at the same distance that the object is in front and also that the line joining object to image is perpendicularly bisected by the silvered surface. Further, some simple geometry shows that all the multiple images lie on a circle drawn about *P*, the junction of the mirror planes.

For the construction of a kaleidoscope a long cylindical box *B* (Fig. 13) is first obtained. A thermos case is very suitable. In accordance with the measurements of the cylinder, cut two strips of mirror together with an identically sized strip of thick cardboard which, formed into a triangular prism *A*, will just fit the interior of the thermos case. The strips should be bound together with masking tape after being wrapped with paper so that the adhesive does not come into contact with the mirror backing. Mark out the size of the triangle formed on the base of the thermos case and with a hammer and chisel cut it out. The hole should grip the mirror prism at the base

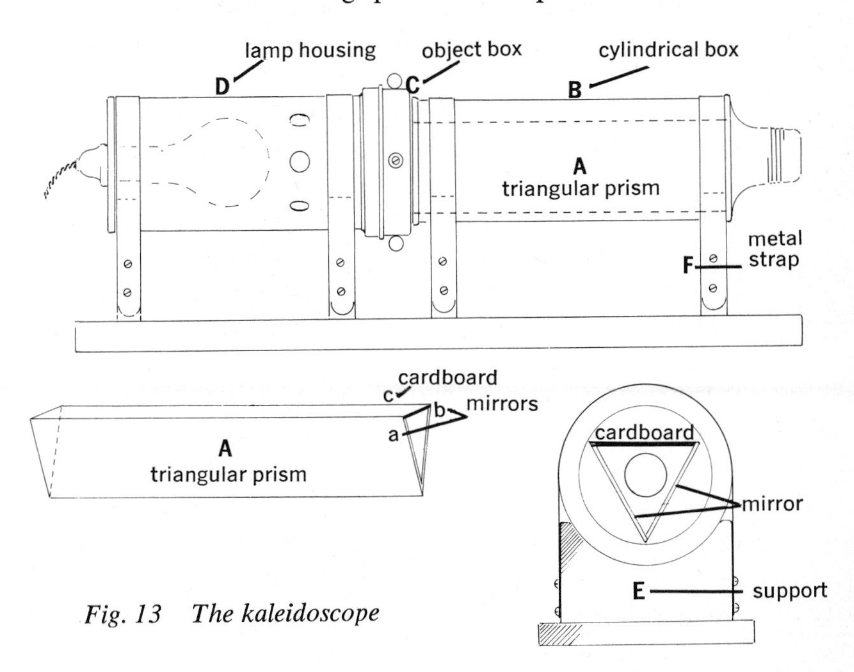

Fig. 13 The kaleidoscope

and a circle of cardboard with a similar triangular hole will retain the other end rigidly in place.

The "object" of which images are to be formed is constructed as follows. Obtain two frosted-glass disks of 3-in. diameter or a suitable diameter for your cylindrical box. Make a shallow box from them, with a ring of thick copper wire or other spacer ⅛ in. thick forming the walls. The box may be either glued together or bound with cellophane tape. Collect variously shaped chips of glass, and face them with bits of colored cellophane. The glass "object box" made should be of such depth as to allow these to fall about freely without overlapping and jamming. One or two short opaque wires or beads may be included provided they are the same thickness as the colored glass chips.

Now, using a cutting scriber, remove clean circles from the lid and base of a 2-oz. tobacco can or other flat can with a fitted lid. Glue the glass object box with rubber cement to the inside of the lid. The lid should revolve easily on its base and three or four knobs should be attached to its outer rim for ease of turning.

The lamp housing *D* for illuminating the object box is made from a can 4½ in. high by 3½ in. in diameter. The base of the tobacco can is soldered onto the rim, where the top has been cleanly removed. The bottom of the can then has a hole cut out with the scriber to take an ordinary lamp socket. Ventilation holes are also cut around the tin, otherwise the heat of the bulb will spoil the colored cellophane in the object box. These ½-in. holes may be cut out cleanly with a sharp centerbit rotated with a brace. In any case the frosted bulb should be of low power, say up to 25 watts, and should not become excessively hot in use.

All that remains is to mount the two units in contact on a baseboard. One good method is to cut circles of the diameter of the thermos case and can with a keyhole saw from two ½-in. boards. Halve these pieces to form four supports *E*. Half-inch-wide straps of metal *F* will then clamp the parts into the supports (see diagrams). The object box should revolve freely against the end of the mirror prism.

As the box portion is rotated slowly the designs viewed are very beautiful and are of infinite variety.

Part two

Sound Mechanics, Oscillations

8
A Galton Whistle and a Bamboo Pipe

If we blow across the top of a tube sealed at the lower end a piercing whistling note may be produced. The action of a whistle may be understood by reference to Fig. 14*b*. A blast of air strikes a sharp edge *E* and by pressure fluctuation the stream flutters from one side of *E* to the other. It is probably redeflected to the opposite side each time the pressure builds up and this results in a series of vortices of air being set up. The "edge-tone" caused by this fluttering of the air is controlled in pitch by the length of the air column set into resonance in the tube. A standing sound wave is set up there. This is really the principle involved in many wind instruments, such as simple pipes, whistles, recorders, flutes, and so on. The main variations lie in how the air stream from the mouth is directed at the edge and how the effective length of resonating column is controlled by stopping holes.

A Galton whistle is a device with a sliding stop that clearly shows the connection between length of air column and pitch of note produced. In its scientific form it can be made very accurately in metal with appropriate

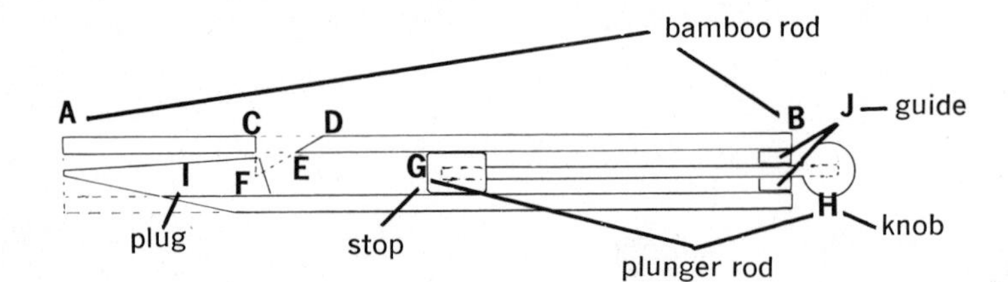

Fig. 14a A Galton whistle

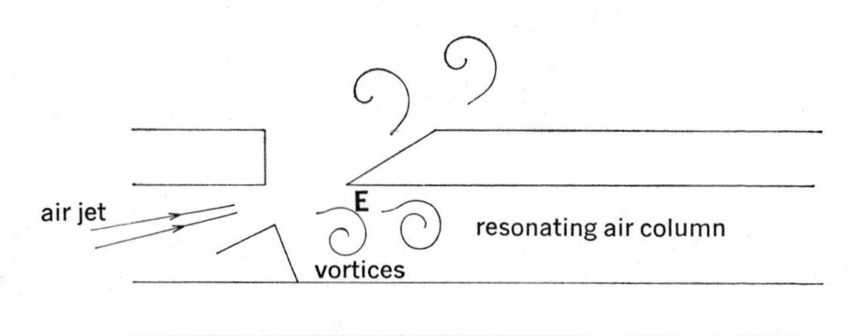

Fig. 14b

numerical graduation of the length of pipe. Experiments may be performed with a simple wooden pipe constructed as follows.

Obtain a length, 6 to 9 in., of bamboo or cane of diameter from ½ to 1 in., *AB* in Fig. 14*a*. Clean out pith and smooth the inside to take a plunger rod *GH*. The stop *G* can be made from wood or cork glued onto the rod and it should slide smoothly in the pipe. Using a fine sharp fret saw, make the straight cut *CF* and the oblique cut *DF*, thereby removing the triangle *CDF* and leaving an acute edge at *E*. Trim a piece of dowel rod which fits inside the tube to make the plug *I*. This is to direct the breath onto the edge *E* as in any whistle. The plug *I* and the guide *J* should be glued in place and the mouthpiece trimmed to shape.

As the whistle is shortened by pushing in the stop by the knob *H,* the pitch of the note rises until it is beyond the range of the human ear, although it can be shown that dogs still respond to these very high notes. The useful range of movement covering the audio band will be found by experiment; it cannot be specified because it depends on the diameter of pipe used.

A more exact instrument can be made with a pipe in brass with a screwed piston, which may be a long large screw. Even so it will be found that the actual pitch of the note is influenced also by the pressure of blown air, and this would have to be constant for correct graduation in frequencies. As with most pipes, over-blowing will cause an octave jump in pitch.

Whistles such as are used by referees and police often have two slightly different pipes or chambers sounding simultaneously. The notes are not identical in pitch and interference between them results in a lower note, known as a difference-tone, being heard. This gives a distinctive penetrating quality to the sound.

Another instrument, which is not too difficult to construct, and is far more musical than the Galton whistle, is a bamboo pipe. Finding a piece of bamboo might not

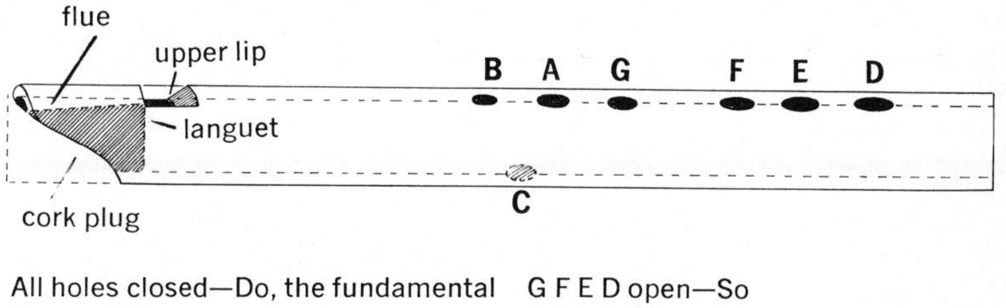

Fig. 15 Construction of the bamboo pipe

be too easy, but most sporting goods stores have inexpensive bamboo fishpoles available, and one of those would do nicely.

Fig. 15 shows how to cut the pipe, once the inside surface has been cleaned up. The holes may be drilled, or even burned through with a red-hot rod, but the upper lip will have to be cut with a sharp chisel or knife. The pipe will speak in the same manner as an organ pipe when it has been fitted with the cork plug, which forms the flue, and the languet essential to directing the air stream onto the upper lip.

The final stage is to tune the notes by boring out the holes, and obviously the mistake of overenlarging them is to be avoided. The holes *D, E,* and *F* are covered by fingers of the right hand, the bottom hole *C* by the thumb of the left, and *B, A,* and *G* by the first, second, and third fingers of the left hand.

Fig. 15 is drawn to scale from an actual pipe of internal diameter ¾ in. Its fundamental note, with all holes stopped, is *D* above middle *D* of the piano. However, the positions of the holes can be altered within reasonable limits to suit the pipe thickness and the hand of the player.

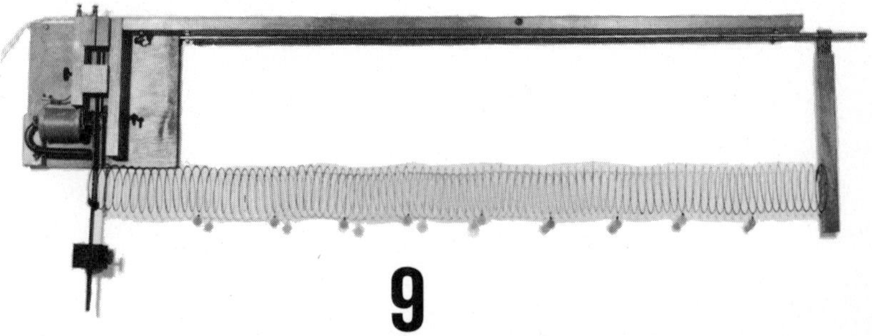

9
A Standing-Wave Apparatus

The model described here is useful in visualizing the mechanism of resonance in a sounding pipe. It shows the mechanical counterpart of stationary sound waves set up in a so-called closed pipe by the vibration of a tuning fork near one end.

The latter is a well-known laboratory experiment in sound which should be studied firsthand before constructing the mechanical analogy. It also throws light on the whistles discussed in chapter 8.

A length of pipe, glass, or metal, is stopped with a cork at one end. A sounding tuning fork is passed transversely to and fro across the open end, while at the same time water is poured in to alter the length of the air column inside the pipe (Fig. 16*d*). For a certain well-defined length of air column, the sound of the fork is greatly

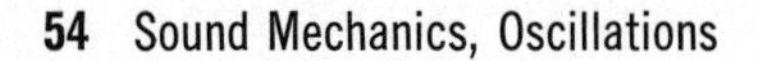

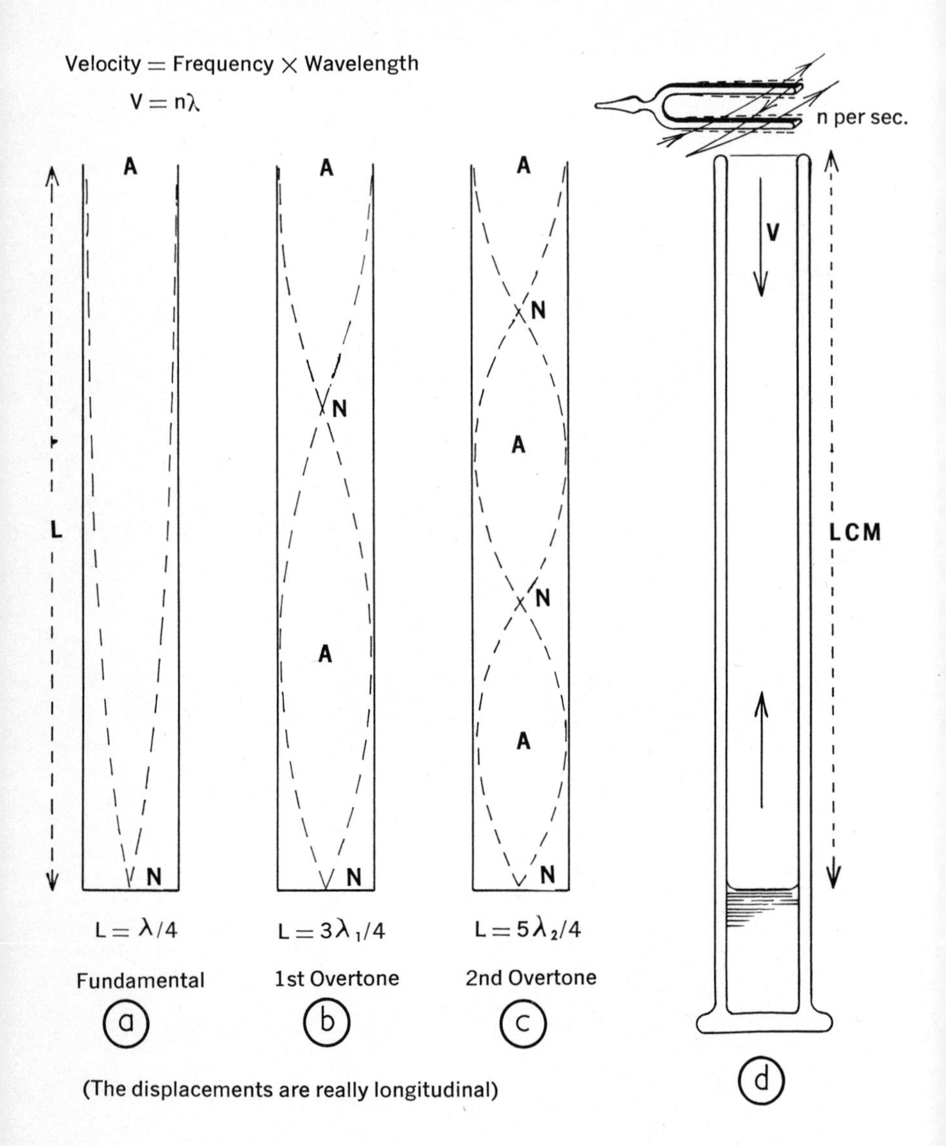

Fig. 16 Stationary wave displacements

amplified by resonance of the air column. Sound waves from the fork pass down the tube with a fixed velocity (appropriate to the air temperature) and are reflected at the bottom end. The two wave-trains may then be regarded as superimposed to produce points of maximum particle displacement at certain fixed spots, called antinodes, and minimum displacement at intermediate points, called nodes. If the pipe is sounding its fundamental note there is only one node (at the closed end) and one antinode (near the open top). This is diagramatically represented at *a,* Fig. 16, though of course the vibrations are lengthwise pulses and not across the width of the pipe. Other possibilities are shown in *b* and *c,* and these higher resonant notes which can be produced are known as overtones.

The down wave-train is set up by a series of regular-interval pressure pulses from the fork while the returning up-wave has its pressure stage exactly synchronizing with that of the fork on returning to it, provided the air path is of correct length. If the water is at the wrong level, i.e., the wrong length of air for this, then the down and up wave-trains will not be in the correct phase relationship to produce the standing waves necessary for resonance with the fork. Different-frequency forks thus require different-length air columns; the higher the frequency or note, the shorter the column. The reader should experiment with resonance by filling a set of test tubes to different water levels. Blown across the top they will sound their fundamental notes, and if eight tubes are available they may be tuned to sound the diatonic scale.

In case confusion should arise, it should be pointed out that where the air movement is greatest (antinodes), the pressure changes will be least, and conversely, for

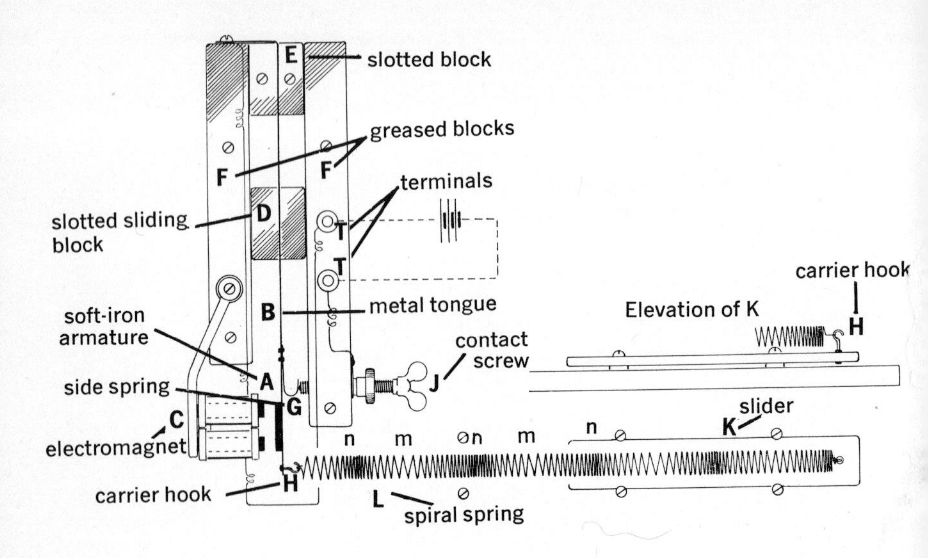

Fig. 17

least displacement (nodes), the pressure changes are greatest.

A fact of basic importance to the physicist is that the speed of the sound wave V is the product of the note frequency n and the wavelength λ:

$$V = n\lambda$$

If we know the positions of the nodes we know λ, since this is twice the lengths between nodes. V can then be found from the known frequency of the fork which is setting up the standing waves.

Now in our mechanical model, represented in Fig. 17, the pressure and rarefaction pulses are set up by a vibrating metal tongue B, tunable to different frequencies. The resonant wave motion is set up and examined in a long coiled spiral spring (really helical but usually called spiral). These waves are along the length of the spring, i.e., longitudinal, and in that respect are like the air-particle movements in a sounding pipe but unlike the transverse movements of water waves on the surface of a pond.

As will be seen from the diagram, Fig. 17, the following components are made up and screwed to a baseboard. Part of a hack-saw blade, with the teeth ground off, is mounted as shown in Fig. 17, *B*, so that the tail end is rigid in the slotted block *E*. A slotted sliding block *D*, a good tight fit on the blade, is mounted to run between greased blocks *FF*, which are accurately planed up to allow *D* to slide, friction-tight, between them. Movement of this block forms the coarse adjustment of frequency.

A make-and-break contact screw *J* normally touches the small side spring *G*, and *J* also serves as a fine-frequency adjuster. Both contact points are tipped with nonoxidizable metal, e.g., platinum wire on the screw and foil on the spring. Actually the make-and-break will work without this for a while, but burned contacts are a continual source of annoyance at a later stage.

Vibrator action is effected by the usual bell-type electromagnet *C*. This is adjustably fitted near the other side of the blade and it acts on a piece of soft-iron armature *A*, soldered or riveted to the blade. To rivet on *A*, *G*, and the hook *H*, the blade must be softened, drilled, and retempered later. *G* is not essential but it gives greater play to the blade and therefore a closer approximation to simple harmonic motion: without *G* the blade gives hard taps on *J* which can, however, produce good wave patterns in the spiral. Wiring of the circuit to the terminals *TT* is obvious from Fig. 17.

The spiral spring *L* most suitable to the other dimensions of the apparatus will probably be found by experiment, but in the author's small model good results are given by careful winding of D.S.C. (double silk covered) Constantan wire, A.W.G. (American wire gauge) 28, on a rod to produce a spiral $\frac{5}{16}$ in. in diameter and some 4 in. long before stretching of the coils. The slider *K* serves to extend the spring to the desired length and the two carrier hooks *HH* are high enough to allow for a little sag in the spring. Magnet wire has also been used successfully, the background then being made white to show up the wave effects.

The springs themselves are rather delicate and are best stored in test tubes, with a straight copper wire pushed down the center of the spring and bent over at the ends. If the soft spring is allowed to fold back on itself the coils will be found to tangle hopelessly.

The photograph on page 53 is of a similarly designed but much more robust wall model. The actual spring of this began life as a toy called Slinky, currently on sale in the toy shops. It is stretched out to some 4 ft. in the model photographed. The adjustable load on the armature tongue permits easy setting of the frequency injected and when resonance occurs the indicator disks, visible below the spring, swing violently at the antinodes while the alternate ones at the nodes remain almost motionless.

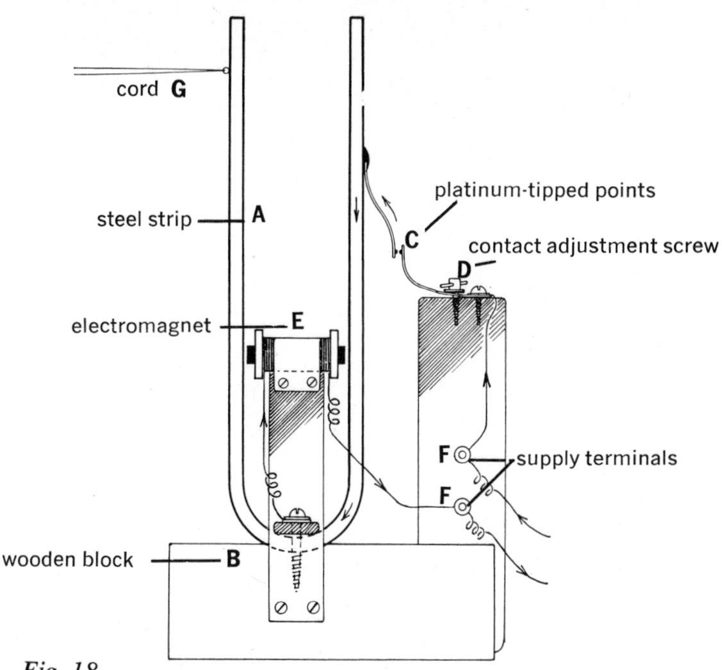

Fig. 18

wooden block *B* grooved to take the bend of the fork. A straight electromagnet *E* pulls in the prongs whenever contact is completed at the platinum-tipped points *C*. These points are carried on light springs which do not appreciably affect the true (simple harmonic) vibration form of the prongs. *D* is a contact adjustment screw. The circuit is completed through the metal of the fork itself and *FF* are the supply terminals for direct current at 2 or 4 volts. The attached cord *G,* in which the transverse waves are set up, passes over a pulley-wheel at the far side of the room.

It is found that current change in *E* does not greatly affect the frequency of vibration, but this can be altered by loading the prongs. The particular model photographed vibrates at 30 oscillations per second.

Either the small adjustable frequency vibrator de-

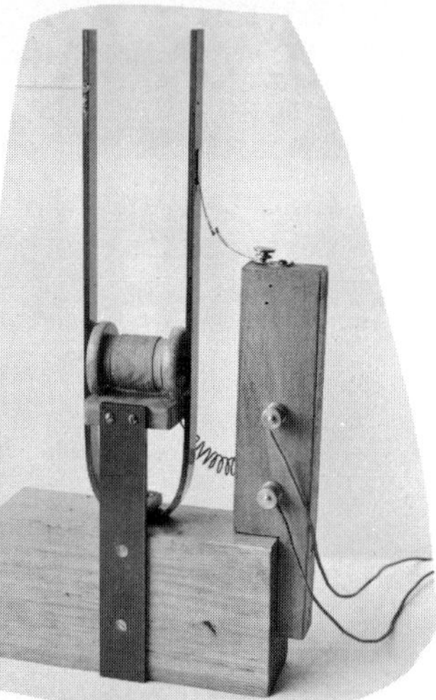

10
Maintained Fork and Melde Arrangements

Before discussing the vibration of standing waves in a tensioned cord we should mention a type of vibrator used in many physics laboratories. A maintained fork is like a large-scale tuning fork which is kept vibrating by means of an electromagnet driven through a make-and-break in just the same manner as the armature of an electric bell.

A large-scale homemade model is shown in the photograph and in the diagram of Fig. 18. As these show very clearly how the apparatus is constructed, explicit instructions for making such a model are not included here but the main requirements are as follows:

The fork is a piece of low-carbon, mild steel strip, 18 by ¾ by ⅛ in., bent into a U-shape, *A,* Fig. 18. Two screws and a metal cross strip clamp it down to a heavy scribed in chapter 9 or this maintained fork may be used to show the formation of Melde loops in a cord. The former is used by replacing the spiral spring by 2 or 3 yards of cotton thread, but the latter is capable of actuating quite heavy string or light-gauge wire.

Attach 3 or 4 yards of strong thread (white if against a dark background, or vice versa) to the hook on the prong of the maintained fork or to the previous vibrator blade and pass the far end over a smooth hook or pulley. Load the free end with some small weight of about 50 gm and after some brief trials it will be found that the string vibrates in clearly defined loops between fixed nodes. Either the length of thread or the hanging load may be varied to produce this result. Experiment soon shows that the actual number of loops depends on the frequency of the vibrator and on the tension in the string. At the blurred widest parts we have the antinodes, and the sharpness of the nodal points makes the experiment fascinating to watch.

There are two different arrangements of the string relative to the blade. If it lies in line with the plane of the blade it is clearly being given a transverse wobble (see Fig. 19*c*), but if it replaces the position of the spiral spring in Fig. 17 it is being given longitudinal pulses (Fig. 19*d*). These two modes of connection should be tried out, keeping the length and tension of the string the same, and it will be found that the number of loops for position *c* is just twice that for position *d*. It may be realized that this follows from the fact that the string in *d* slackens off alternately in its up and down positions for consecutive movements of the blade to the right, and therefore it indicates a frequency half that of the vibrator, whereas in position *c* the string movements coincide with the blade movements. The point of attachment of the

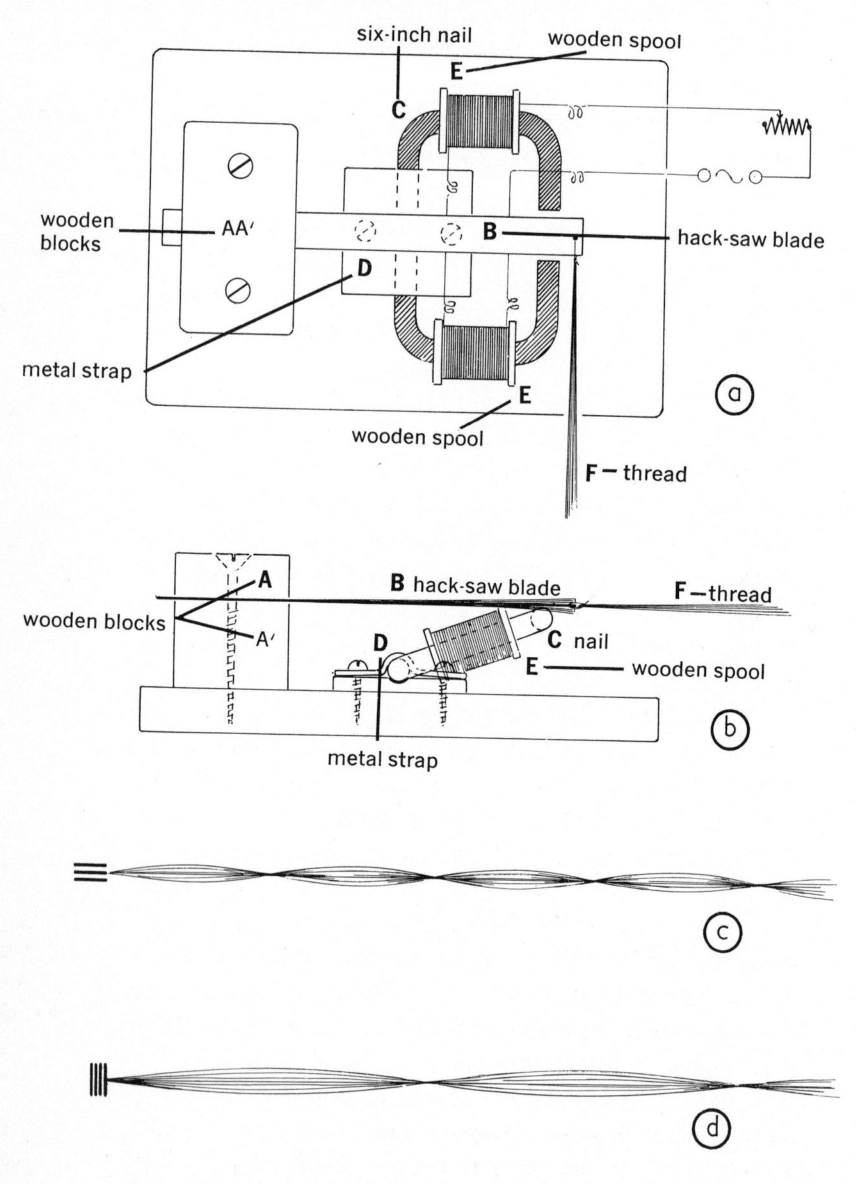

Fig. 19 Melde experiments

string to the blade may look like a node due to the much bigger movement of the string at the antinodes, and for this reason any measurement of loop length would be better made away from the actual ends of the string.

An interesting form of Melde apparatus uses the fixed frequency of regular A.C. house lines to drive the vibrator, and for those readers who prefer to make this type the following details may be helpful.

Two blocks of hardwood *AA′* clamp down some 3 in. of softened hack-saw blade *B,* as in the plan and elevation of Fig. 19 *a* and *b*. A 6-in. nail is bent to the shape *C* to form the core of an electromagnet. The arms of this are wound with a few dozen turns of A.W.G. 23 D.C.C. (double cotton covered) copper wire. With care, and using adhesive tape, this may be done without the use of the spools shown in Fig. 19. In any case the final bending of the poles inward is liable to break up wooden spools, and if they are used it is easiest to reglue their split halves together after the core has been bent to shape. The electromagnet naturally must be wound so as to produce unlike polarity at the free ends of the core, the polarities alternating with reversals of the A.C. Care must be taken in crossing from one coil to the other and this is clearly shown in Fig. 20. By means of a strap of metal, *D* in Fig. 19, screwed over the middle of *C* and thereby stiffly hinging it, the level of the poles can be raised or lowered. The poles should be just below the level of the blade, but adjustment gives the best position and when this is found the screws should be tightened up to clamp the electromagnet.

Step the current down to 6 or 12 volts by means of a transformer and, preferably adjusted by a rheostat, the current is fed to the electromagnet. Now very little movement of the blade will occur unless it is in resonance with

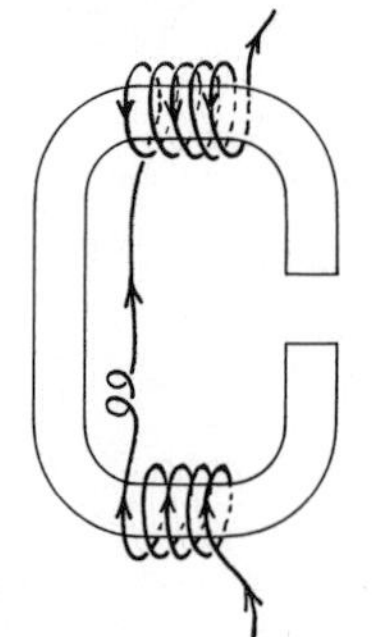

Fig. 20

the A.C. frequency. A small degree of quivering, called forced vibration, may be noticed. However, by altering the length of blade projecting from the clamping blocks it can be given a natural frequency of 120 cycles per second. The tugs of the electromagnet on the blade are then synchronized with this fundamental frequency of the spring and it acquires a really large vibration and blurred appearance. This is a case of resonance, and in itself forms an instructive experiment. To physicists it is an important phenomenon to comprehend, both mechanically, as here, and in its electronic counterpart. A minute quantity of energy is being injected into the system at just the right instant of each cycle. This makes up for losses which would otherwise damp out the oscillations, and thus their amplitude is maintained.

Why, you may wonder, should the vibrator blade have a frequency of 120 c.p.s. when the current is known to be 60 c.p.s.? Look at the graph of the alternating current, Fig. 59*a*, page 160, and it is clear that this has two biggest values of current (+ and −) in each 1/60-second cycle, so that there are 120 biggest magnetic pulls per second. Each pull tends to drag the iron tongue into the maximum magnetic flux, i.e., directly between the poles, and it therefore makes 120 oscillations per second.

If now a small hole has been drilled through the end of the blade or a terminal tag soldered to it, the thread or thin colored string may be attached as previously suggested.

A common school physics experiment is to find the frequency of house current with such an apparatus. It involves weighing a length of the string to find the mass per centimeter (say, *m* gm per cm). Next, some clear nodes are obtained and the length of loop (say, *l* cm) is carefully measured. The only other quantity needed is the tension in the cord *T*, and this is found in "dynes" by multiplying the hanging weight in grams by 981.

Since the frequency of the vibrating cord *n* is given by $n = \frac{1}{2l}\sqrt{\frac{T}{m}}$, we are able to find *n* by substitution and consequently the current frequency, which is half of this.

Most electromagnetic vibrators of the bell type will run well on D.C. from a storage battery at 4 to 6 volts, but a rheostat in the circuit will be found very useful in controlling energy input into the spring.

Frequency adjustment will quickly result in the characteristic nodal points *N* and antinodes *M*. The mechanism of the wave formation is made very obvious and is fascinating when viewed under the stroboscope (see chapter 23), especially the effect of gradual frequency alterations from static wave conditions.

11
Sound-Wave Representation—Crova's and Cheshire's Disks

Crova's disk is designed to illustrate progressive-wave motion by rotating a system of eccentric circles, while Cheshire's does the same for standing-wave motion.

The diagrams should be drawn in India ink on thick, smooth, white cardboard or on good-quality, smooth, white paper mounted later on a plywood disk some 12 in. in diameter. In both cases the disk is to be rotated behind a front mask—a 12-in. square of plywood with a radial viewing slot about $\frac{3}{16}$ in. wide cut out with a fret saw. A nut and bolt, with suitable washers and lock nut, pivot the disk centrally on the back of the mask. Also a handle —a bolt with a loose tube or bead on it—which is screwed to the back of the disk serves to rotate it. The bolt head should not break the flatness of the diagram surface.

Crova's Disk

Fig. 21 shows the required system of circles. A 5-mm-radius circle is drawn at the middle of the cardboard. As shown in the enlarged detail *b,* divide its circumference into 12 equal parts and number the points, 1, 2, 3, 4, etc. With center 1 draw a circle of 1-cm radius, then, progressively increasing the radius by 5 mm (or by 4 mm if patience permits), continue drawing circles from the marked centers 2, 3, 4, 5, etc., until the diagram is as large as required.

As the card is spun and viewed through the slot it is observed that the particles make concertina-like movements about fixed rest positions, though the disturbance

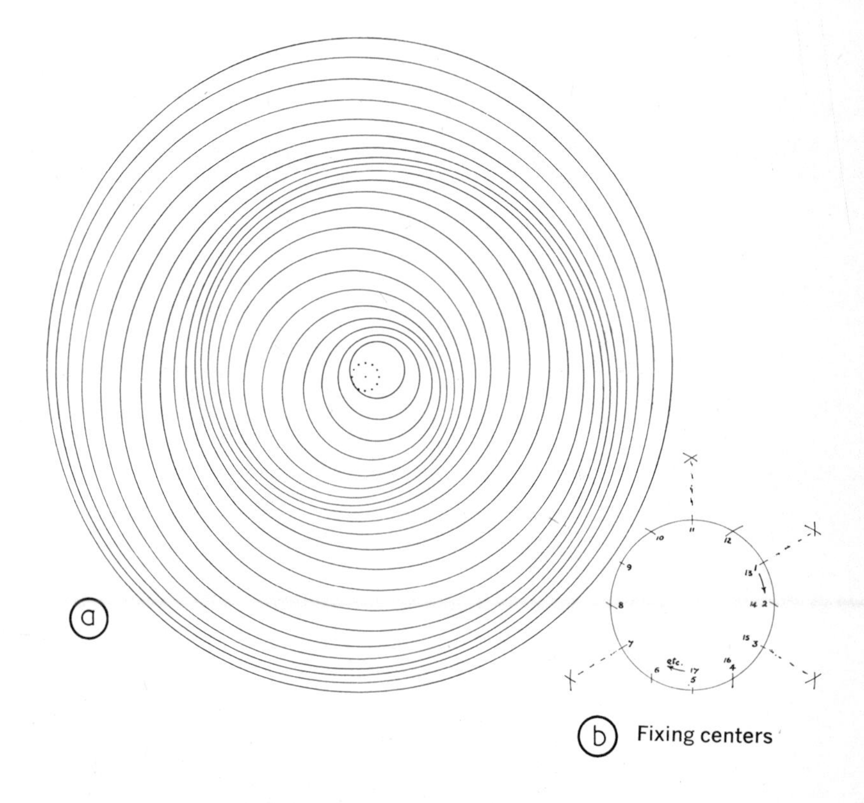

Fig. 21 Crova's disk illustrates progressive waves

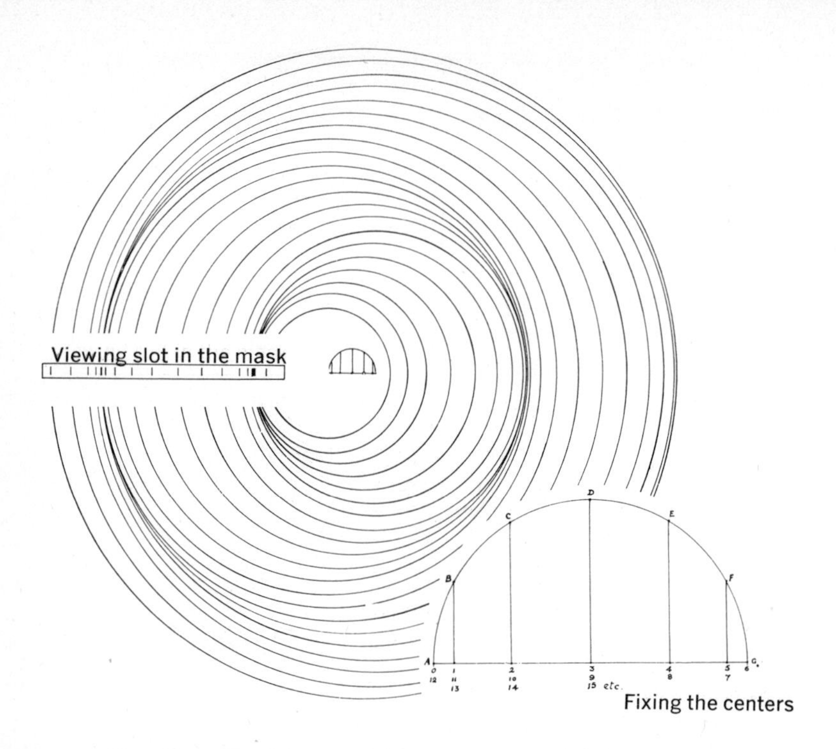

Fig. 22 Cheshire's disk illustrates standing waves

itself is seen to move radially across the slot, outward or inward according to the direction of rotation of the handle. As in sound propagation this is representative of a traveling wave.

Cheshire's Disk

As in Fig. 22, draw a semicircle, 1-cm radius, and divide it into 6 equal parts. Drop perpendiculars from the dividing points *A, B, C, D, E, F* onto the diameter and number the projection points in succession as shown in the enlargement. Using these points 0, 1, 2, 3, 4, etc., as centers, in turn describe circles from them, increasing the radius by an equal increment of, say, 5 or 6 mm each time. The centers travel back and forth across *AC* until the diagram adequately fills the cardboard.

Although again the portions viewed through the slot appear to concertina in and out as the wheel is spun, the wave does not appear to move radially along the slot but is stationary. This in fact illustrates the compressive type of oscillation shown by the spiral spring of chapter 9 and the air-particle oscillations in a resonant sounding pipe.

12
The Cartesian Diver

The Cartesian diver is a model which will amuse younger brothers, as well as demonstrating and clarifying some basic hydrostatic principles.

The foundation consists of a small inverted test tube or bottle. The lower end is left open, but a large cork is drilled to fit over the sealed end as in Fig. 23*a*. Bind on two pieces of copper wire, about gauge 19, with adhesive tape and bend them to form arms and legs. Before hammering out the ends into hands and feet cut off sufficient wire for the figure to float just submerged to the top of his hat. With a sharp knife or razor blade trim the cork to form the head and hat of the diver; then decorate him with paints as a frogman or any fantastic figure. After thoroughly drying him and checking that he still just floats, place him in a deep glass jar (a quart mayonnaise jar would do). Fill the jar with water, cover the top with a piece of rubber sheet, such as an old inner tube, and bind this down with string effectively to seal the top; then trim off the surplus from this flexible cap (Fig.

23*b*). Control the diving of the figure by pressure on the top.

The principles demonstrated are these:

i. The pressure applied to the enclosed fluid is distributed equally throughout it, being exerted in all directions on the boundary surfaces, up as well as down.

ii. The increased pressure on the air in the inverted tube reduces its volume (Boyle's Law), i.e., more water enters the bottle.

iii. The body is supported in equilibrium when its over-all weight is just the same as the weight of water it is displacing. This is a case of the so-called principle of flotation.

iv. Entry of more water increases the density (weight/volume) of the figure to a value greater than 1 gm

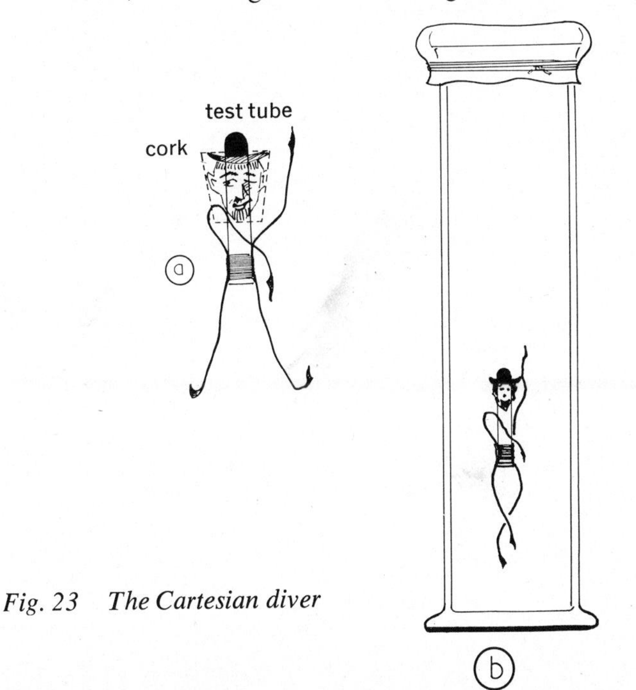

Fig. 23 The Cartesian diver

per cc, and when this happens he dives. Then release of the pressure expands the air, reduces his average density to less than 1 again, and he surfaces.

If the lower end of the tube has not been painted over, the water can be seen to enter as the pressure is applied. By making the opening small and tangential, sudden release of pressure expels a jet of water which will twirl the diver around as he rises.

One commercial model is made of black glass in the form of a devil with a long tail, and the perforated tip of the tail admits the water for diving.

13
The Propeller

Probably future generations will see jet reaction as almost the only propulsive force for aircraft. However, aviation has been well served by the air screw, and marine propulsion is still dependent on the screw or propeller.

Clearly the screw blades must have some resistant medium to bite on and the higher the propeller speed the greater is the air compression, air density, and resultant bite.

The toy described below exemplifies this principle well and takes only a short time to make.

The rotor can be made from the lid of a can cleanly cut out with a rotary can opener. The only provision here is that the outer edge shall be rolled, to avoid any subsequent danger from cuts. Carefully draw the three blades on the lid (Fig. 24*a*). Sections marked *D* may be completely cut out. The cuts are best chiseled through on a block of wood with an old chisel. Before giving the blades their twist, punch or drill at the center two $\frac{1}{12}$-in.-diameter holes separated $\frac{1}{12}$ in., then remove the little bridge of metal between them to make a central slot.

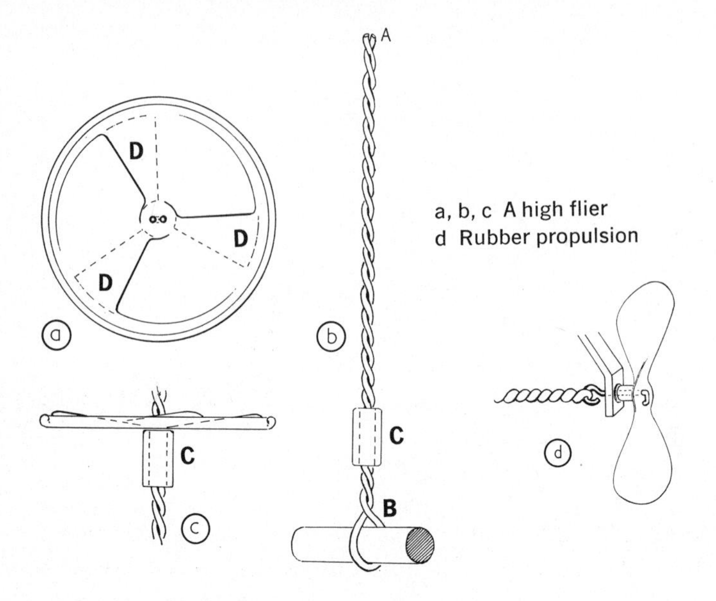

Fig. 24 Methods of screw propulsion

The next requirement is a twisted strip of thick metal about ¼ in. by 10 in. to fit the above slot. As this may not be readily available you may prefer to use two strong wires, galvanized fencing wire or welding wire from a garage, as shown in diagram Fig. 24*b*. To twist the wire, fold a 2-ft. length in half with a large loop at the bend. Slip a rod through the loop and clamp the free ends close together in a vise. Then twist up the doubled piece to give a long uniform twist of angle about 20° to the axis. The holes in the rotor may need a little trimming so that it will spin freely up and down the twist. Finally, obtain a tube *C* which slides easily along the wire. Tin may be rolled up for this purpose.

The angle of the rotor blades must naturally be such

as to give lift when the rotor is spun by being pushed off the wire.

There are three parts to this assembly. The wire, held vertically; the tin tube, which should rest on the loop at the foot of the twisted wire; and the rotor, which should rest on top of the tin tube. To launch this flying saucer, hold the arrangement steady above your head by the tube and strongly pull the wire twist down with the other hand.

Since the whole thing is quickly constructed, you may wish to experiment with different blade angles, or with different numbers of blades from two to six, in order to obtain the optimum effect of high flight. These tests will presumably be made out of doors, and height and distance competition may possibly be arranged with a like-minded friend who has constructed his own high flyer.

Propellers of the form shown at *d* are easily cut from sheet metal. With a rubber-band drive they are a familiar source of power both on model airplanes and model boats.

14 Jet Propulsion

Most of us have at some time laid down a garden hose and been surprised, and possibly wet, by its reaction to the jet of water. The rotary garden sprinkler works on this principle and certainly the force needed to hold a hose is well known to the fireman. It may not have occurred to you, however, that this is the same jet reaction driving airplanes at immense speed. On earlier craft the slanted aerofoils or wing flaps give lift as the propeller drags them forward: on jet aircraft the plane is pushed forward by reaction to the jet. The explosive backward thrust is partly against the air itself and partly on the exhausted explosion gases.

Those who have acquired a Bunsen burner, or have made one, as in chapter 1, may like to make a simple model in illustration of the principle.

First obtain a small round tin can *A,* Fig. 25, 1 in. or so in diameter by about 2 in. long. Alternatively, a disk the size of a quarter may be soldered on to the end of a tube. Very accurately find the center of the inside of the can, preferably using a separate disk with a central hole, and there knock a depression with a conical punch. This is to serve as a bearing. Next, make right-angle bends in two short pieces of ¼-in. copper tube *B,* make holes in the can to fit the copper tubes, and solder them radially onto the tin. Make sure that they are of equal weight and radius, filing them if necessary until the system balances vertically on a pencil point. Make the central pivot the sharpened tip of a spiral of wire *C,* fixed to the barrel of the Bunsen.

For the water trough around the barrel of the Bunsen

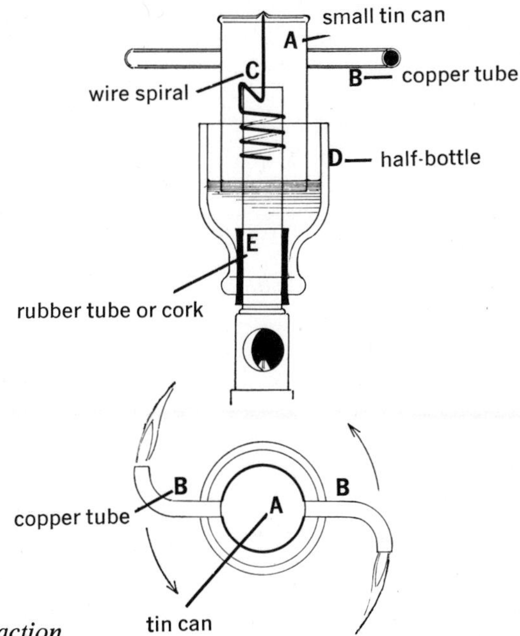

Fig. 25 Jet reaction

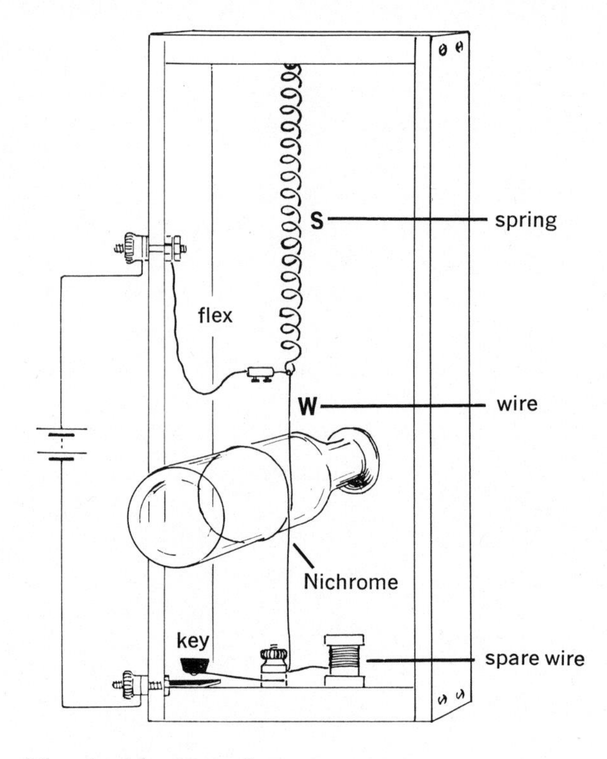

Fig. 26 A wide glass-tube cutter

burner, you will need to cut a bottle in half. Find a suitable bottle, about 2 in. in diameter with a rather narrow neck. A frame or a bracket can be quickly put together to hold about 8 in. of Nichrome wire (A.W.G. 28 or 29). In Fig. 26, *W* is the wire and *S* the spring, easily made from piano wire. First scratch around the glass at the required position with an ordinary glass-cutter, then wrap the Nichrome wire around the scratch. Heat the wire to bright redness by passing a current at perhaps 12 to 20 volts through it. It is sometimes necessary to touch the glass with a drop of cold water to make it split, but it will be found to crack cleanly around the line as a result of the strain of unequal expansion. The sharp edge should then be ground off on the emery wheel for safety in handling.

The neck half of the bottle is inverted, *D,* and fitted to the Bunsen burner barrel either with a sleeve of rubber tube *E* or with a drilled cork as in Fig. 25. It forms a trough in which the bottom edge of the rotor is just submerged in water and seals off the gas there. If the spinner is well balanced the unlighted gas will just cause it to rotate slowly, but for obvious reasons this test should not be very prolonged. Again, with the Bunsen air holes closed and yellow gas flames burning at the jets the speed of rotation is slow. However, with the air fully on and long blue jets burning, the rate of revolution is quite fast. The main limitation appears to be the viscous friction of the air and the water seal.

15
Simple Harmonic Motion

Simple harmonic motion (S.H.M.) is a mathematically exact motion in which the displacement from a fixed point is proportionate to the acceleration toward that point; but as long as the displacement (amplitude) is small we may think of the vibration of a point on a twanged spring or of a pendulum bob as being nearly simple harmonic motion. More exactly, an S.H.M. is the projection on a diameter of a circle of the motion of a point moving with uniform angular velocity around its circumference.

Imagine a fine, inked brush *B*, Fig. 27*a*, attached to the end of the vibrating spring *A*. If the strip of paper *C* is steadily drawn along beneath the brush, it draws a trace which is known to the mathematicians as a sine wave. This is characteristic of S.H.M. drawn out along the axis of a graph. The tip of the brush is executing a nearly pure simple harmonic oscillation.

Such a trace, incidentally, is the pressure fluctuation graph of the air when a note of the simplest type (pure tone) is sounding. It also represents a fluctuation of electromagnetic properties in light and radio waves, and you will appreciate that it is, therefore, an extremely important representation of a variety of physical happenings. Regarded as graphs of pure notes, then, Fig. 27*b* portrays a higher frequency or pitch than *c*. Graph *b* is also one of smaller amplitude than *c*, i.e., represents a softer note; *c* has the greater displacement and energy associated with it and this implies a louder note.

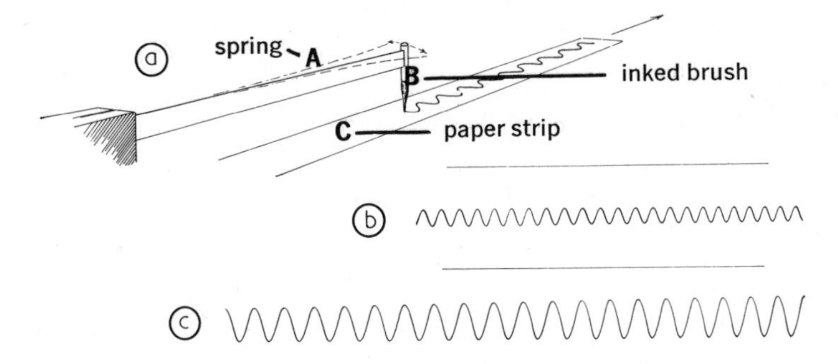

Fig. 27 S.H.M. and sine waves

16 Compounded Harmonic Motions

A swinging pendulum bob, if the amplitude of swing is not large, executes a close approximation to simple harmonic motion. This type of reciprocating motion has already been defined as one in which the acceleration of the particle toward a fixed point is always proportionate to the displacement from that point.

Now let us imagine a body which not only has the S.H.M. type of oscillation in the one direction but simultaneously another S.H.M. at right angles to it. Its motion, then, is a more or less complicated path depending in shape on three factors—the relative amplitudes of the two swings, the relative starting point (phase difference) of the swings, and on the relative frequencies or number of oscillations per second.

Suppose the first swing starts at A and the second at A' as in Fig. 28*a*. The joint movement will be the slant line to and fro along AC. But if the second swing starts at A', as in *b*, the combined motion is a circular path. Any other starting point would produce an elliptical path *c*. Again, if the lengths of swings AB and $A'B'$ were different an ellipse would result. The foregoing applies to motions of the same time period, i.e., a 1:1 frequency ratio, but if the number of swings per second is different, very complex motions would ensue. The simplest results would be obtainable if the frequencies were in some simple whole-number ratio such as 1:2, 1:3, 2:3, etc. The paths then resulting are known as Lissajous Figures and their study is fascinating. Figures of some of the simpler ratios are indicated in Fig. 33 on page 92. Many forms of apparatus, including the Cathode Ray Oscilloscope, will give perfect transient pictures of these traces and several different types of harmonograph will draw them.

Obtain a straight length of steel clock spring about 15 in. long and ½ in. wide (a long hack-saw blade might serve) and soften an inch in the middle by heating it red-hot. Clamp it in the vise and give it a right-angled twist with pliers. It should again be heated red-hot, chilled in cold water, cleaned with emery, then brought down to blue, thereby retempering it to spring elasticity.

Slot, then glue onto one end, a ½-in. wooden ball or

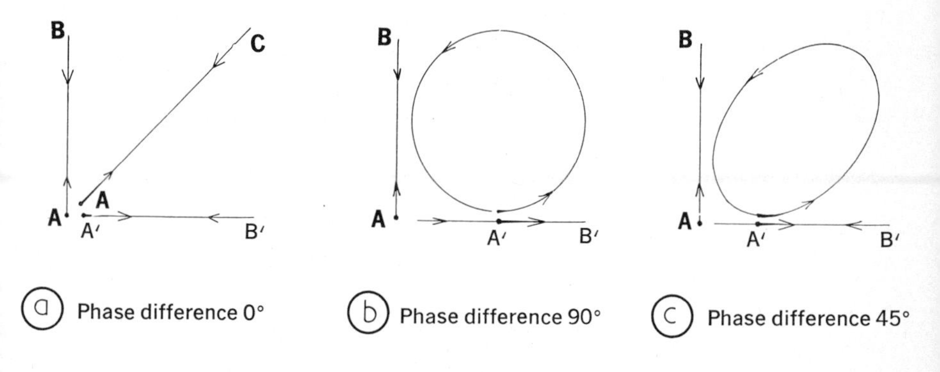

Fig. 28 Compounded oscillations

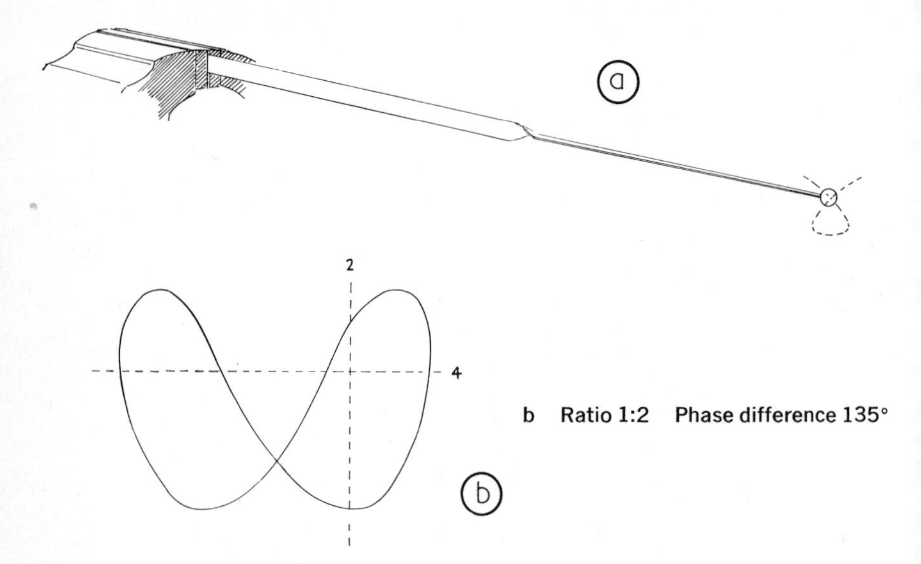

Fig. 29 Lissajous Figures

bead. Paint it black except for an end spot of white or luminous paint (see Fig. 29*a*).

If, with the other end of the spring clamped in the vise, the bead is pulled to one side, say in the horizontal plane, and then released, it vibrates with simple harmonic motion. The end view of the white spot, due to persistence of vision, gives a straight line. Displaced vertically, it describes a vertical line in the same manner.

Now if pulled aside obliquely and released, it describes a compound movement, a Lissajous Figure. This, if the frequency ratio is a simple one, will be a very recognizable simple loop, e.g., an ellipse, a U-shape, an alpha-shape, or an S-form. The simple ratios 1:2, 2:3, 1:3 are quickly obtained by adjusting the projecting length of spring. The frequency of the portion from bead to twist is fixed, but the total length gives a slow periodicity which is capable of variation, at right angles to the faster fixed one.

It is possible to attach a fine insulated wire to the spring and solder it to the center pin of a round-tipped flashlight bulb bound to the end of the bare spring with copper wire instead of the bead. This gives a very effective luminous trace of the Lissajous Figure in a dark room.

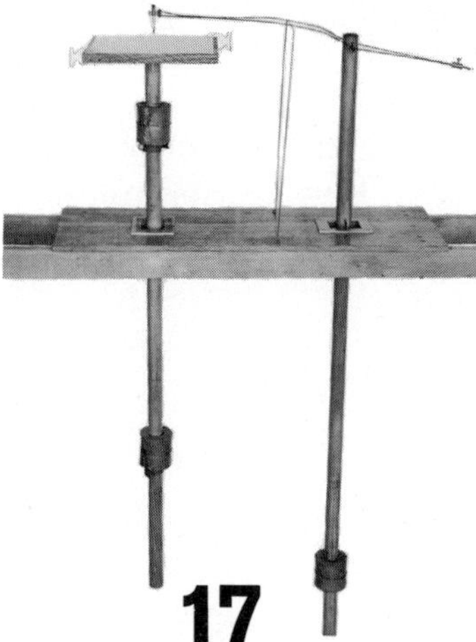

17
A Harmonograph

The type of harmonograph described here consists of two pendulums swinging at right angles, one carrying a platform holding a piece of paper and the other the pen which describes the trace (Fig. 30). The trace drawn is a harmonogram.

Each pendulum is of the type known in physics as compound. A compound pendulum differs from a simple pendulum in that its mass is distributed throughout its length instead of being concentrated in a bob at the end of a so-called weightless string. The pivoting position determines the time period and it may be observed here that for one particular time period four such suspension positions exist in the rod. The time periods will in our case be varied by moving the loads, above and below the pivot, and not by moving the pivoting point, which would upset the relative positioning of the pen and paper.

The basic requirements are simple. Obtain two good straight broomsticks, *A* and *B*, and cut them to a length of 3 ft. 6 in. Treating the rods similarly, saw the top end truly perpendicular to its length. Measure 1 ft. from that end and drill a close group of ¹⁄₁₆-in. cross holes exactly central and perpendicularly across. Hammer a short length of hack-saw blade through these holes to link them up in the form of a slot. Soften an old hack-saw blade by heating red-hot and then cooling slowly. Cut off two 2-in. lengths and file, or grind on the emery wheel, one sharp edge (Fig. 31*a*). These will form the two "knife edges" (Fig. 30, *CC*) when knocked through the slots in the rods. Get half a dozen adjustable hose clamps which will fit the rod. These are for supporting the weights in position on the rods by clamping beneath them. If the slots have been cut too large, or if the knife edges are not precisely perpendicular to the rod, you may

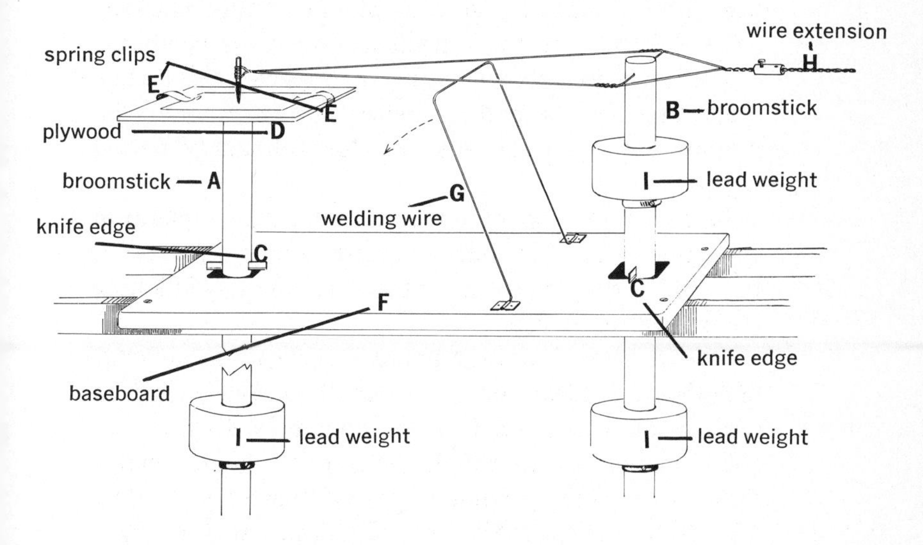

Fig. 30 Harmonograph

find it necessary to fix hose clamps above the knife edges as well.

The weights themselves may be cast from lead in tin cans, and three should be made. Roll a tube of tin so that it just slides freely on the broomstick and then fix the tube centrally in place in an empty fruit can. This may be done with a piece of tin shaped as shown (Fig. 31*b*) after sealing it to the bottom of the can with plastic metal. Melt scrap lead in an old pot and when the lead is thoroughly molten run this into the annular space between the tube and can, taking great care to avoid burns by spurting or accidental leakage of the lead. When cold, cut out the circle of tin from the bottom of the tube and smooth off the rough edges at each end. Good weighty rings of lead (Fig. 31*c*) may be made in this manner.

An alternative to the above method is to obtain sheet lead from a hardware store or plumber. Then cut long strips 2½ in. wide and roll them around the pendulum rod to form weights. A casing of tin will preserve the shape and also keep the hands clean in handling the weights, but in any case the outer turns should be tacked down.

Screw to the top of one pendulum rod a platform consisting of an 8-in.-side square of sturdy plywood *D*, Fig. 30. Spring clips *EE* at the sides of this will hold the trace sheets in place.

Obtain an old drawingboard (a cheap rectangular breadboard is ideal) or a 2-ft. length of 8-in. plank, to serve as the baseboard *F* of the apparatus. Drill corner holes preparatory to chiseling out two 1½-in. squares through which the pendulum rods will pass. Cut shallow 45° *V*-grooves in the sides of the holes as at *d*, Fig. 31. Indent four pieces of tinplate similarly into the grooves

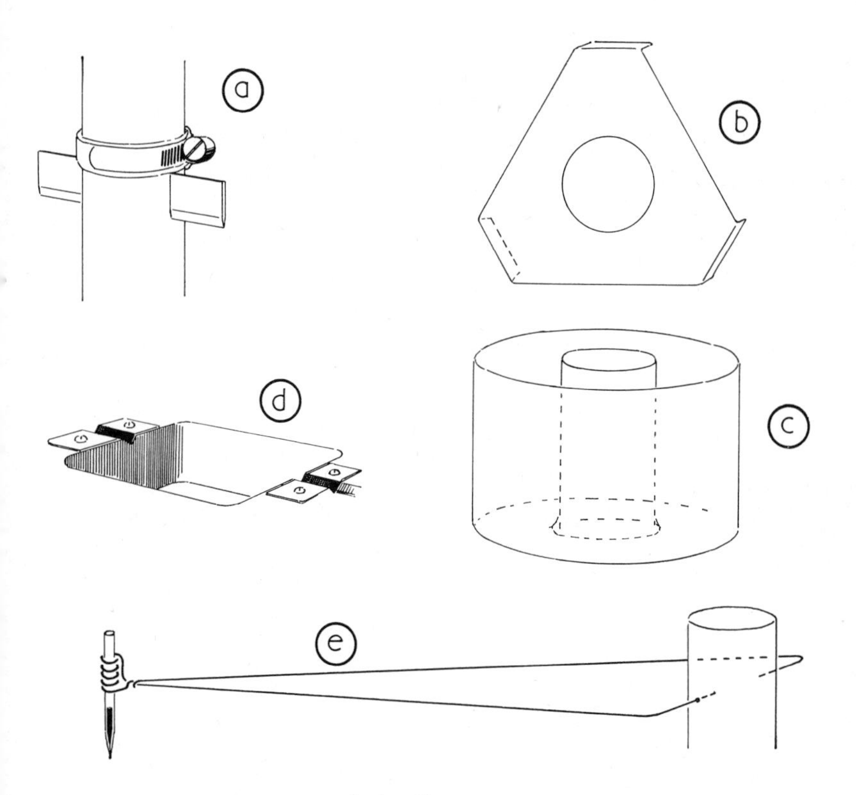

Fig. 31 Harmonograph details

and screw them down to make bearings harder than the wood for the knife edges.

The penholder lever is made from welding wire bent as shown at Fig. 31*e*. The ends of the wire turn into a $\frac{1}{16}$-in. hole accurately drilled near the top of the appropriate pendulum rod, while the middle of the loop is coiled so as just to grip the pen. If the pen and holder are light enough no counterpoising extension beyond the pivot will be necessary. But the friction of the pen on the paper should be kept low and this can be achieved by soldering on the wire extension H with its adjustable weight, shown in Fig. 30. The pen is lowered onto the paper after the pendulums are in motion by turning down the friction-tight loop of welding wire G, Fig. 30. When at rest the pen should just descend centrally onto the paper platform and stand vertical.

Rest the board between two tables of equal height or otherwise clamp it rigidly so that the pendulums are free to swing. Set the weights so that the swings are in a known simple ratio of frequencies and proceed to experiment with different starting points for the two rods. To obtain a required phase difference demands some practice.

An inexact ratio will result in a changing pattern as the phase difference alters slowly and the result may be an exquisitely intricate design with watered-silk effects. Slow decrease of the amplitude produces this fascinating complexity of lines, making the growth of the pattern toward the center most interesting to watch. However, the simpler shapes with only a few loops completed are the more scientifically useful.

It will be found simpler to make the pen-moving pendulum the slow time-period one, since a load can quickly be added to the top section above the pivot of this rod, and with weights balanced above and below the frequency is very low. Trial with both weights, one, or none at all, will soon show the range of swings available. Naturally, the heavier the loads the greater the inertia: the amplitude is then maintained longer and the loops are very close-packed.

To produce really beautiful traces a specially smooth and fine pen is essential, though for coarse work a weighted ballpoint pen refill can be made to function. The finest pens are best made from glass tubing, as in

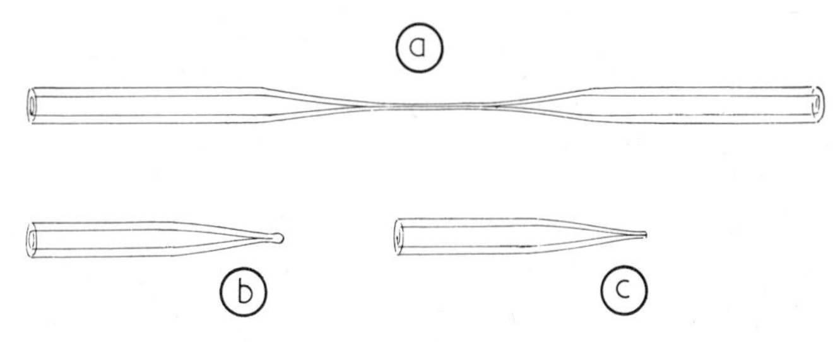

Fig. 32 Pen making

Fig. 32. Draw out the tube, after softening in a small Bunsen flame, to give a rapid taper (Fig. 32*a*). Cut and seal off the two tubes, *b*. Rotating the tube all ways on a smooth oilstone, rub down the tip until the capillary hole appears, *c*. The pen so made should show no sign of catching or roughness in writing. It may need to be suitably weighted to give the correct writing pressure in the lever. Use a black ink which does not, by quick drying, clog the pen, and the smoothest white paper available. A poor quality, such as smooth duplicating paper, will serve for the numerous trial runs.

Try to work scientifically by noting the frequency ratios and phase relations on each record. Mount them neatly and make a folio or book of your most perfect harmonograms. They should be grouped, classified according to frequency ratio, and the first diagram in each case should show one or two swings only, before the pen has been lifted.

The illustrations in Fig. 33 have been chosen for clarity of ratio rather than for their beauty or complexity, and for these Lissajous Figures, for example, the following superscriptions would be adequate:

(*a*) Frequency ratio, 1:1
Ellipses show a phase difference of less than 90°.
(The latter would give a circle.)

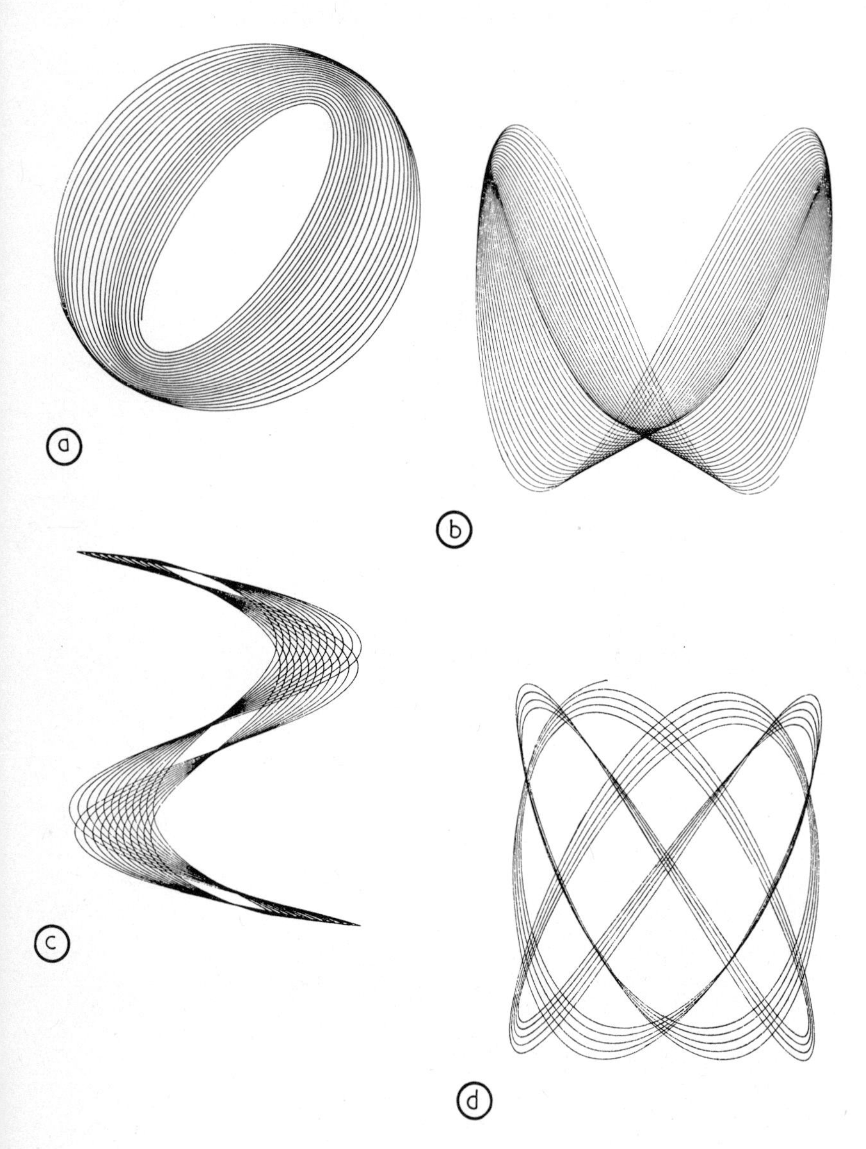

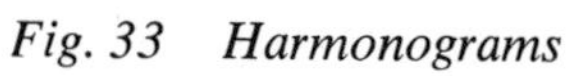

Fig. 33 Harmonograms

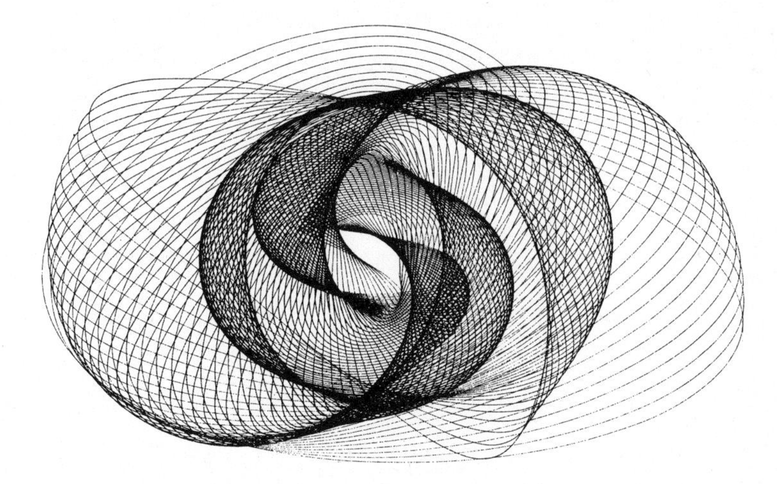

Fig. 34 An example of a more complex harmonogram, the result of coupling an elliptic with a linear S.H.M. in frequency ratio 1:2, but with a slow phase swing. The elliptic pendulum carrying the platform is on a gimbal-type support.

The amplitudes are seen to be decreasing at different rates.

(*b*) Frequency ratio, 1:2
The initial phase difference of 45° reduces to 0°, the *U*-shape. (90° would give the figure-8.)

(*c*) Frequency ratio, 1:3
(Counting the crossings which one loop makes across two straight lines drawn at right angles, i.e., 2:6, enables us to find the ratio.)

(*d*) Frequency ratio, 3:4
An open figure showing a few loops with a phase difference of 45°.

Perhaps in conclusion it should be added that Lissajous Figures as drawn by harmonographs are of no practical use; whatever virtue the work embodies lies rather in the manipulative skills acquired by the operator. Many of the more interesting byways of pure science, perhaps fortunately, have no foreseeable practical application.

18 A Pfaundler Spring Apparatus

Another interesting model for the visual display of Lissajous Figures employs a pair of vibrating springs carrying slotted plates. Its construction can be developed as follows:

Cut out the flat bases of two tin cans some 2 to 2½ in. in diameter, using a can opener; then diametrically across each circle cut a narrow slot 1½ in. by 1/16 in. This can be done by curving the disk and sawing the slots with a hack-saw blade. Solder each disk to a length of straightened clock spring, as shown in Fig. 35*b*. For soldering steel, zinc chloride is an easier flux to use than the usual resinous flux. The other end of each spring is hammered tightly into a slot cut with a fret saw in a block of hardwood *S*. These blocks are screwed to the base of a rectangular box so that the springs are at right angles and the disks, near one corner of the box, vibrate just clear of one another, the springs being above and below the disks. The slotted disks are painted with matte black paint, as is the rest of the box interior.

One spring *C* is used at its full length to give the lower

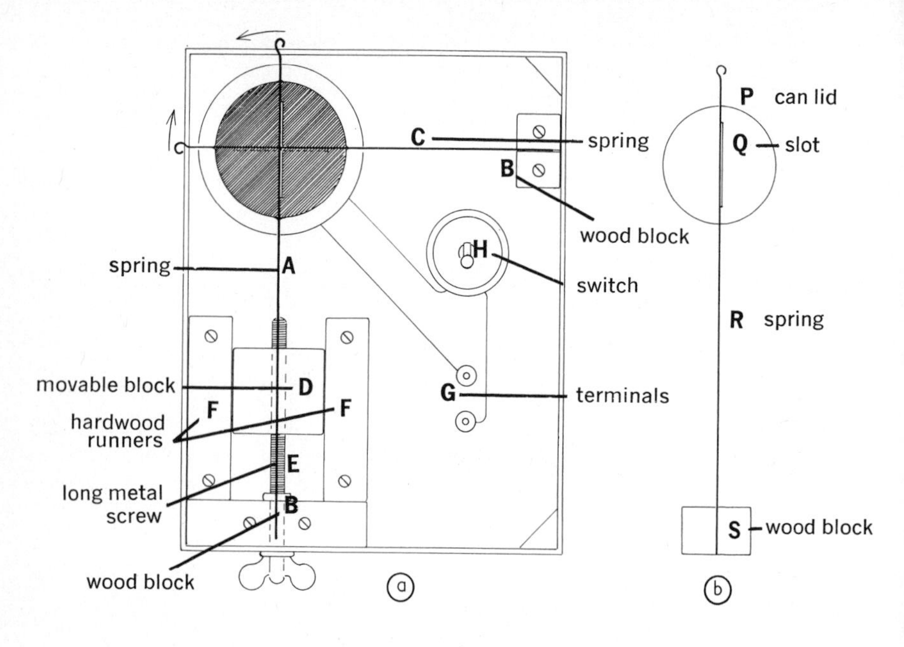

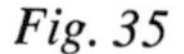
Fig. 35

frequency, but the other is to be adjustably shortened to give frequencies up to three times this number. A block of hardwood *D* has a fret-sawed slot cut in it of the thickness of the clock spring. This movable clamp-block is also drilled with a parallel hole below the slot and tapped to take a long metal screw *E*. A suitable screw used by the writer was from a broken C-clamp. When turned, this thumbscrew, projecting through the side of the box, pushes the sliding clamp-block to and fro along the spring, so varying the length free to vibrate. The sliding block must be a very good fit on the spring, allowing no play, yet not gripping so tightly as to buckle the spring when drawing it back. The block slides between hardwood runners *F*, as shown in Fig. 36*a*. These runners, the slot, spring, and control screw are all well lubricated with graphite grease. Before being soldered onto the disks, the free ends of the springs may have been softened, then twisted with round-nosed pliers into loops by which they may be twanged. At this corner, the encasing box sides are cut out so that the loops are accessible for twanging.

Again, for viewing the figures, a 1½-in.-diameter circle is cut out from the lid of the containing box above the disks. A flashlight bulb is mounted below the disks and covered over with a diffusing screen of translucent material, e.g., a plastic jar-cover or the ground-glass cover-slip of a gas-collecting jar.

With both slotted disks at rest a small spot of light is seen. If one spring is vibrated the image seen, by persistence of vision, is a white line perpendicular to that spring. Obviously movement of the other spring only gives a line at right angles to this one. Simultaneous vibration of both the springs, therefore, produces the usual Lissajous Figures, of which a wide range is obtainable by varying the frequency ratio by the screw control and by changing the phase by the relative moment of release.

There is room in the box for a battery, but if an external current source is preferred, terminals *G* and a switch *H* are added to the box as shown.

Other details are left to the constructor, but a useful addition on the lid is a neatly printed frequency-ratio scale traversed by a pointer attached to the sliding clamp-block. Finally, as with other models, accuracy of workmanship should be aimed at and clear varnish or paint used to give a pleasing finish.

Part three

Magnetism, Electricity

19
Mapping Magnetic Fields

All magnets are surrounded in space by an associated field, the particular direction of which, at any spot, is that in which a single north pole placed there would try to move. Such an isolated N-pole does not, of course, exist, but it is possible to imagine one if it is far enough away from its S-pole partner. The cross section of such a field pattern is easily investigated in the case of fairly strong magnets by the well-known iron-filing method.

Lay flat on a table any arrangement of permanent magnets you happen to possess and, after noting where the N and S poles lie, proceed as follows. Overlay the magnets with a piece of thin white cardboard or any paper-covered thin tray not made of iron.

If you do not possess any iron filings they may be simply made, if a trifle laboriously, by filing down a large nail held in the vise. The filings are sprinkled from a salt shaker thinly and evenly over the card. When the

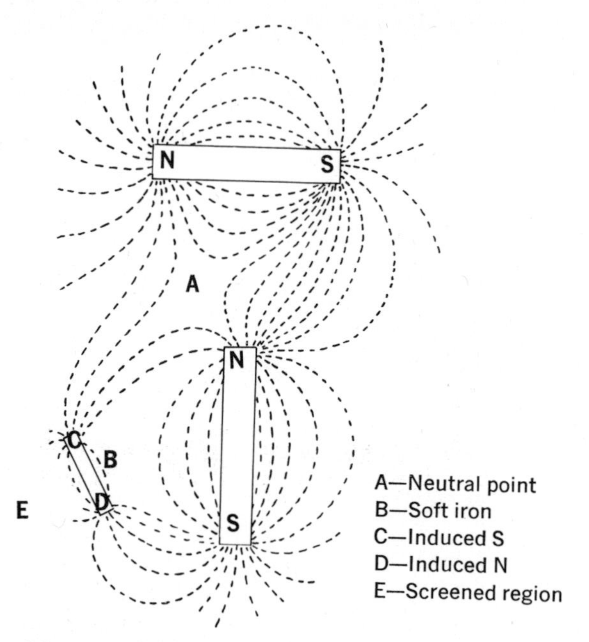

Fig. 36 Magnetic field map

cardboard is tapped gently the iron dust will be seen to set in streamers indicative of the shape of the field, as in Fig. 36.

It will be noted how they appear to link the poles of opposite polarity and avoid crossing between like poles. Also, where the field is most intense above the poles the whiskery groups stand up on end and for that reason appear to be less concentrated there. The intensity distribution is more correctly seen when the board has been carefully lifted away from the magnets.

The patterns are so effective that you will want to preserve permanent records of your best efforts. Three methods for this are therefore suggested:

i. Make the filing pattern on photographic printing paper in a darkroom, using a red lamp. Give the correct exposure to the filing-covered paper from an electric light and then develop the print in the usual manner.

ii. Use paper heavily waxed by being dipped in a tray of molten paraffin or candle wax. When the filings are in the most effective arrangement, melt them into the wax to produce a fixed pattern.

iii. Spray the arrangement of filings with black ink either by means of a perfume atomizer or an air brush.

For the third method you may like to try out the old technique used in making decorative prints of pressed leaves. Place ⅛-in. depth of black ink in a saucer and

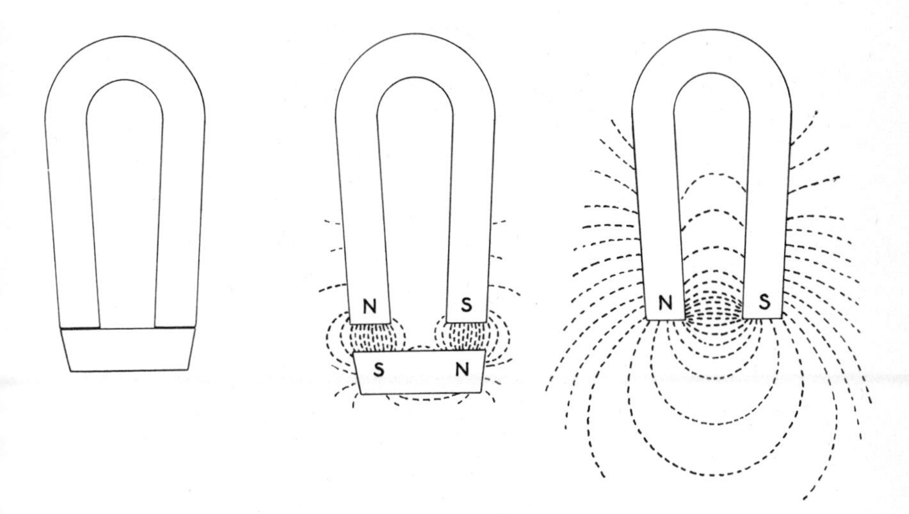

Fig. 37 Effect of keeper on a field

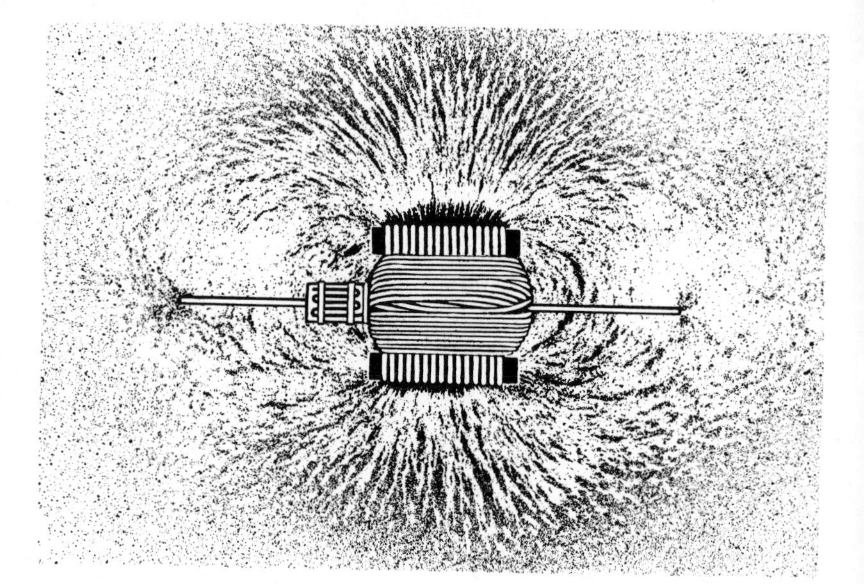

Fig. 38 A splatter-work picture of the field of a current-carrying armature. Drawing of the armature position has been added to the sprayed field.

dip into it an old soft toothbrush. Then rub the toothbrush to and fro on an old comb or a piece of screening held horizontally about 6 in. above the filing design. A fine spray of ink results and makes a shadowgraph of the arrangement. Do not allow ink to accumulate on the underside of the comb or whole drops will fall off and ruin the work.

It is advisable to spread old newspaper widely around the scene of operations and some practice with the process is required to avoid blots, but it can give excellent results.

It should be remembered that the magnetic pictures

are just cross sections of fields which actually penetrate all directions in space. Some of your records should have, besides bar magnets, soft-iron keepers showing screening effects, horseshoe magnets, and electromagnets, all labeled and well displayed.

20
Current Measures

There are three primary effects of a current of electricity, viz., chemical, magnetic, and heating (the latter including lighting). Each of these may be made the basis of a method of measuring current. The first is used only for very exact work in research and for the calibration of other instruments. Most of the commercial ammeters in everyday use depend for their action on either of the other two.

In the magnetic class a few employ a moving magnet, some a moving-iron assembly, and others use the repulsion induced in soft-iron cores. All the better class of instrument, however, employ a delicate coil of wire which twists in a magnetic field according to the current flow in the wire. The very sensitive measurers of thousandths or millionths of an ampere are always of the moving-coil type and are called milliammeters and microammeters, respectively.

We do not propose to discuss the moving-coil form here, not only because it is of such general availability but also because it does not normally measure alternating current, only direct current. We shall confine our attention to two simple types of ammeter which, with reasonable care and skill, make useful instruments, the scales of which can be adapted to either D.C. or A.C.

A Moving-Iron Ammeter

The moving-iron ammeter depends for its action on the pull of a solenoid, a cylindrical wire coil exerted on a partially entered iron core. This ammeter could be used to test the current in a circuit attached to an ordinary storage battery.

Roll up a cylinder of tinplate (sheet iron) about ¼ in. in diameter by 2 in. long. A double thickness of tin wound on a rod can be neatly soldered up to form the moving-iron core *A*, Fig. 39.

Then make a solenoid *B* of insulated copper wire on a tube of thin cardboard 2 in. long and with a ½-in. hole. Two or three layers of enameled magnetic or D.C.C. wire of about gauge 25 is suitable and it may be held in place with a binding of cellophane tape. The ends of the coil should be brought out to terminals T_1 and T_2 on the baseboard, and preferably insulated from it.

A hook is soldered to the top of the core and attached to a silk thread *C*, which passes over a very small tube or pulley-wheel *D*. This turns freely on a thin, round-headed brass center screw. The other end of the thread is attached to a light spring *E*, anchored to the backboard at *F*. The spring may be either of the form shown

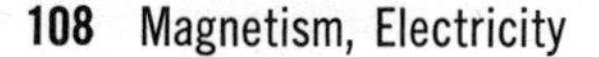

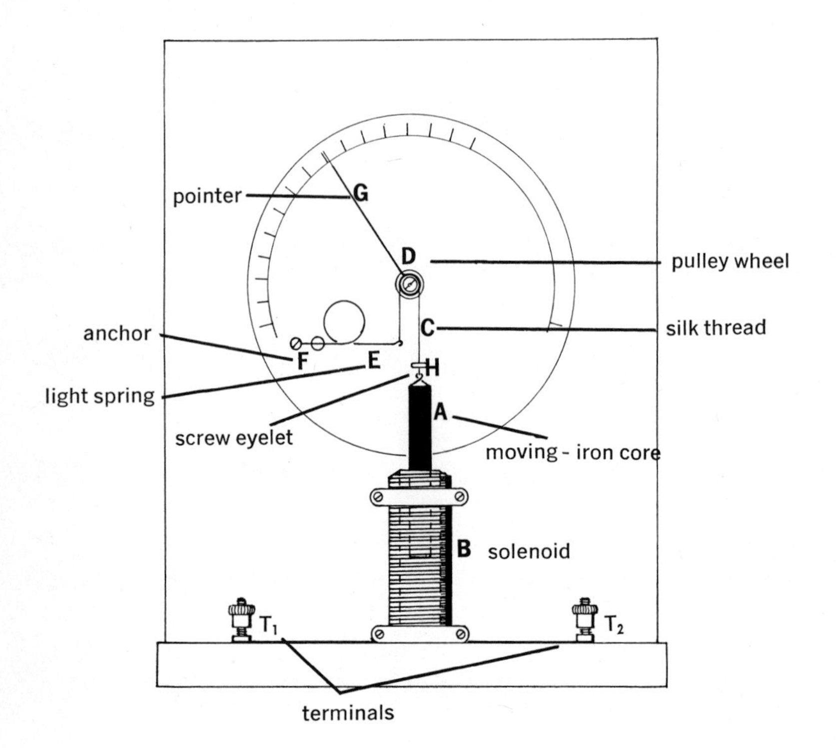

Fig. 39 Soft-iron attraction ammeter

in Fig. 39 or a weak vertical spiral spring. Incidentally, such springs are very easily made from a fine-gauge piano wire simply by wrapping it around a suitable-sized rod clamped in a vise. The instrument pointer *G*, made from the same steel wire, is joined to the little pulley *D*. If the latter is a ½-in. length of quill glass tube the wire may be bent around and glued on with epoxy glue, but no doubt would be best soldered on in the case of a metal pulley. In any case, the pointer should just clear the surface of a circular paper disk stuck onto the back-board and centered on the pivot of the pulley.

The action of the meter is obvious enough, since the core is pulled into the coil with a force somehow dependent on the current, and returned to zero by the spring when no current flows. One cannot expect the scale to be linear with the current, i.e., evenly spaced divisions, and therefore the dial must be scaled or calibrated against another good commercial ammeter, which may have to be borrowed for the purpose. This is put in series with the homemade instrument (see Fig. 40) and then a current controlled by a suitable rheostat is sent through the circuit. In any single loop such as this the current is the same in all portions. Great care must be taken not to overload the good ammeter. Therefore, begin with the maximum resistance and never reduce it to a point beyond which the good ammeter reads its full-scale deflection. With each increment of current carefully mark the new scale behind the pointer. Should the pointer be disarranged later it is easily reset to the zero mark for zero current, since the pulley is just friction-tight on the thread.

For obvious reasons the meter must be used upright. A small screw eyelet *H* around the thread at the upper limit of the core prevents the latter from falling about in transit. The meter casing and other details must now be left to the ingenuity of the constructor, but plastic boxes

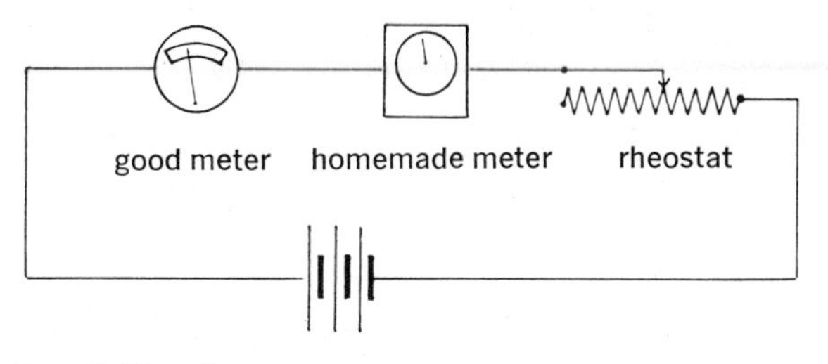

Fig. 40 Calibration

are recommended as being dustproof and of high insulation.

A Hot-Wire Ammeter

The last mentioned of the three effects of electric current, i.e., heating, is the activating force of the hot-wire ammeter.

A length of some 5 in. of thin Nichrome wire (A.W.G. 28), *AB* in Fig. 41, is stretched between two rigid pillars which in turn are joined by thick leads to terminals T_1 and T_2. The midpoint of the wire is held down by a spiral spring *C*, the lower end of which is attached to the baseboard. The upper end, hooked around the wire, keeps it continually in tension and takes up the sag of expansion. Also joined to the same central point is a link of wire *D*, hooked at both ends. The upper end is joined to the silk thread *E* and thence to the weaker tensioning spring *F*. The thread, in fact, is in a balanced position between the two springs, but the length and therefore the sag of the hot wire *AB* determines the actual position and not the Hooke's Law recovery of the spiral spring. Details of the pulley and pointer actuated by the thread are precisely the same as for the moving-iron ammeter. Current through the resistance of the thin wire heats it sufficiently to cause sag due to expansion and this is recorded on the scale.

Calibration of this scale is carried out exactly as for the moving-iron ammeter. Comments on protective casing also apply here. The wire link *D* in this meter prevents heat from *AB* burning the thread *E*. Naturally *AB* should lie well clear of any material liable to scorch and the maximum allowable current should not make the Nichrome wire glow an even dull red. One of the worst

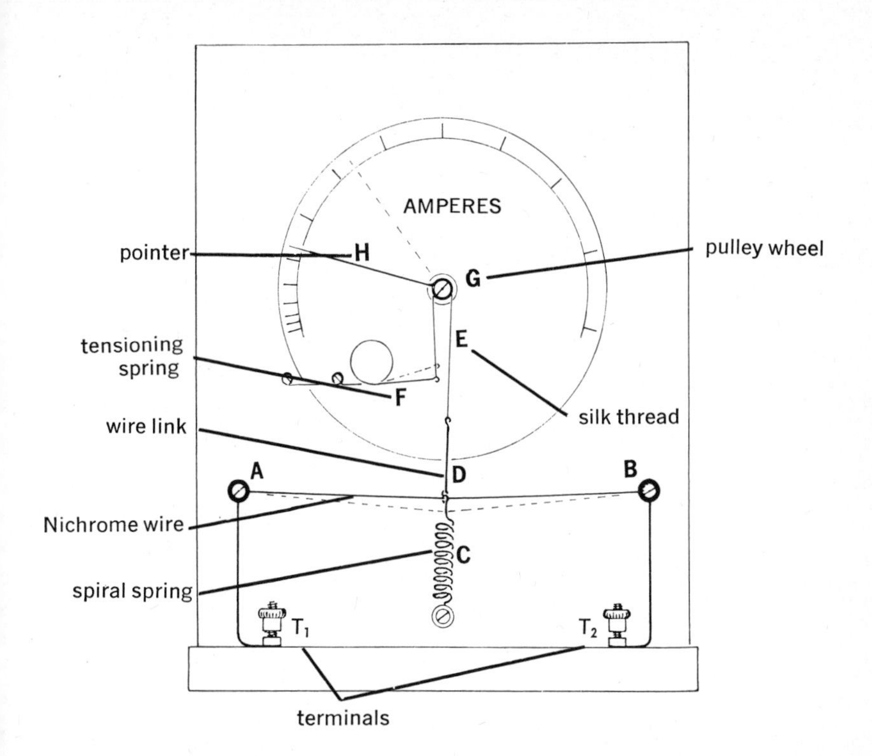

Fig. 41 Hot-wire ammeter

features of this type of meter is that an overload will burn out or damage the wire, necessitating its replacement.

We must here make reference to the peculiar spacing of the scale divisions. In this case the heat generated and therefore the expansion and the pointer movement are proportional to the *square* of the current measured. The resulting square-law scale is crowded at the zero end and more and more widely spaced toward the maximum end. Briefly, Joule's Law describing the heating effect of current is symbolized

$$H = I^2Rt$$

where H means joules of heat energy, I is the current in amperes, R is the resistance of the wire in ohms, and t is the time of flow of current in seconds. Thus: Heat generated varies with $(\text{current})^2$.

If one is more familiar with calories as units of heat it may be added that the number of joules may be converted into the equivalent number of calories by dividing them by a factor approximately 4.18 (called Joule's Equivalent).

A great virtue of the hot-wire ammeter is that it can record alternating current and direct current. Obviously heat is generated, whichever direction current passes through the wire. Thus, besides the D.C. scale the meter may also be calibrated in A.C. divisions. These units are referred to as root mean square, or R.M.S., values of current.

Alternating current is continually increasing and diminishing in value and changing in direction so that the peak value is not the effective current. R.M.S. values represent a kind of equivalent D.C. and any particular reading is approximately 0.7 of the peak value of the fluctuations to which the alternating current rises. In any case, the calibration is simple enough, since all that is necessary is to replace the storage batteries of the circuit, Fig. 40, by an A.C. source, such as a transformed-down house-current supply.

21 A Solenoid Motor

The magnetic-field intensity in a coil depends on the number of turns and on the current flowing around them. This model demonstrates the principle that soft iron is attracted into the strongest part of the magnetic field of a solenoid. The loops of force, which have magnetized the core by induction while current is flowing in the coil, may be visualized as tending to contract, pulling in the soft-iron armature (Fig. 42).

First make the solenoid former *B,* Fig. 43, from some nonferrous tube with end brackets attached. This could be from an old bicycle pump or ½-in. copper water pipe some 3 or 4 in. long. The brackets should be rigidly attached to withstand the later winding, either by soldering or by spreading the tube ends, *A,* Fig. 43. Wrap the

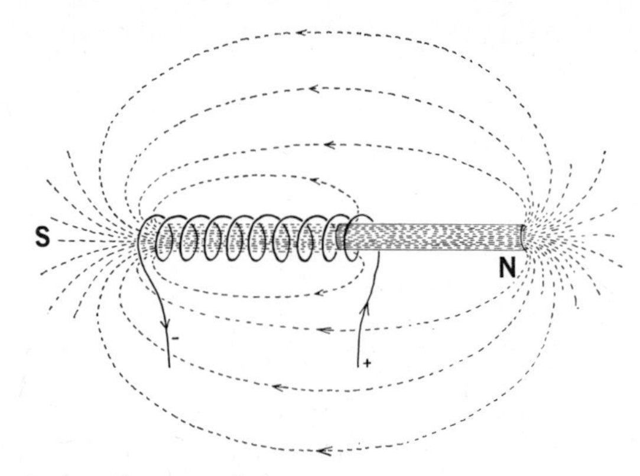

Fig. 42 Induced magnetism

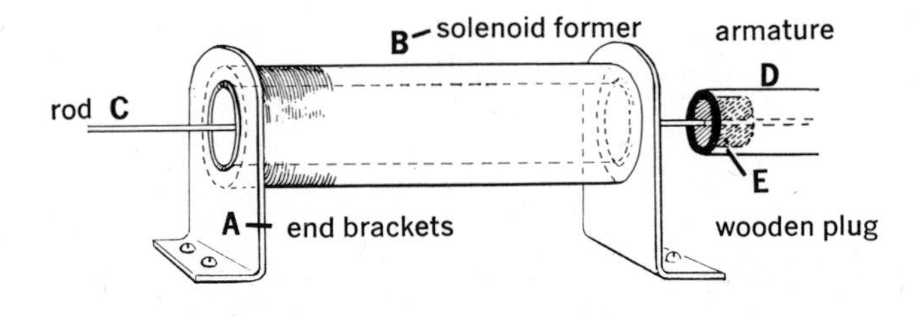

Fig. 43 The solenoid

tube *B*, using an improvised winder, with some 6 to 12 layers of D.C.C. wire of gauge about 21 A.W.G.

The armature slides on a rod *C*, which can be welding wire from a garage, a metal knitting needle, or a bicycle spoke, but it must be straight, smooth, and centrally located in the tube.

For the armature itself, *D*, wrap two thicknesses of soft-iron sheet, cut from a tin can, around a suitable rod by rolling it underfoot in the right direction. Solder up the tube and insert ¼-in. wooden end plugs *E*, centrally drilled to slide freely on rod *C*. The armature should be about the length of the solenoid and of such diameter as to leave a clearance of ⅛ in. between it and the hole. It is laminated (made up of more than one layer) to make it more permeable and therefore more strongly magnetized by induction than a solid-iron armature would be. Steel would of course be unsuitable since it would acquire permanent magnetism. This sliding core should also be fairly light in weight to reduce inertia.

At this stage the bent crank-rod of the flywheel could be made. A knitting needle can, with care, be sharply bent so that the ends are still in alignment, and the length by which this flywheel axle is cranked should be half the total throw of the core in the solenoid. At its outward limit the core should still be in the coil by about 1 in. overlap. Do not roughen the axle in the bending process and check parallelism of the parts very carefully.

Now a linkage loop or connecting-rod of bent welding wire, *A*, Fig. 44, is removably hinged onto the core *B* and wrapped on the crank *C* as shown in the diagram.

A flywheel can be constructed in the same manner as in chapter 3, page 26. It should not be exactly

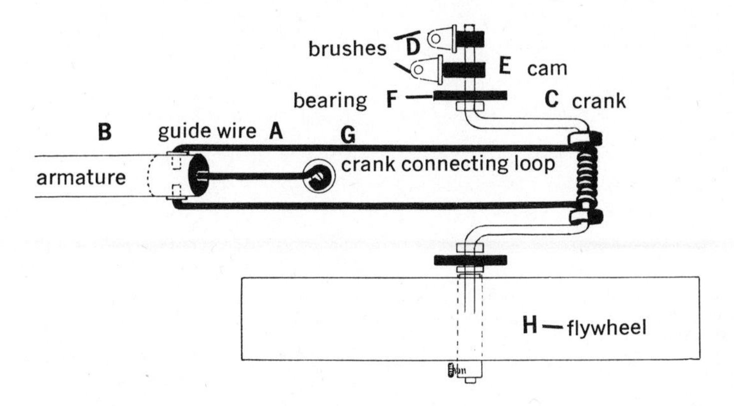

Fig. 44 Linkage with solenoid core

balanced with the lead strip, but biased with a heavy side, to be later clamped diametrically opposite the crank. A brass tube with an inset-screw, such as an electrical barrel connector, is soldered through the middle of the flywheel. By means of it the wheel may be clamped in correct position on its axle.

The coil is to be energized by flow of current; in other words, contact is to be made for about one-quarter of each time of rotation. This must occur while the core is actually traveling into the coil. The circuit is therefore completed by a cam mounted on the flywheel axle, a second bearing and brush making permanent contact.

The current path can be followed in Fig. 45. Entering at the right-hand terminal T_1 it flows around the solenoid *B*, passes to the brush momentarily in contact with the cam *E* on the axle, through the shaft itself and the permanent brush contact *F*, and so back to the left-hand terminal T_2. The small cam *E* should be friction-tight at first, correctly adjusted relative to the crank, then finally soldered into position. Brushes may be made from springy phosphor-bronze strip. Weather stripping is a useful material for this and can be cut with scissors. Incidentally, a useful source of brass washers, spacers, angle-pieces for bearings, and so on, lies in the curtain-runners and small brackets found in dime stores.

Suitably proportioned, well oiled at the bearings and correctly adjusted, the motor will run at good speed from a battery-charger or from a 6-volt car battery, but it has no appreciable power beyond that needed to drive color disks and very light models. It is, in fact, disadvantageous to make this model heavier or from more robust parts, since it will only move more sluggishly.

As with many electrical models, the efficiency may appear to fall off after a period of running and the trouble

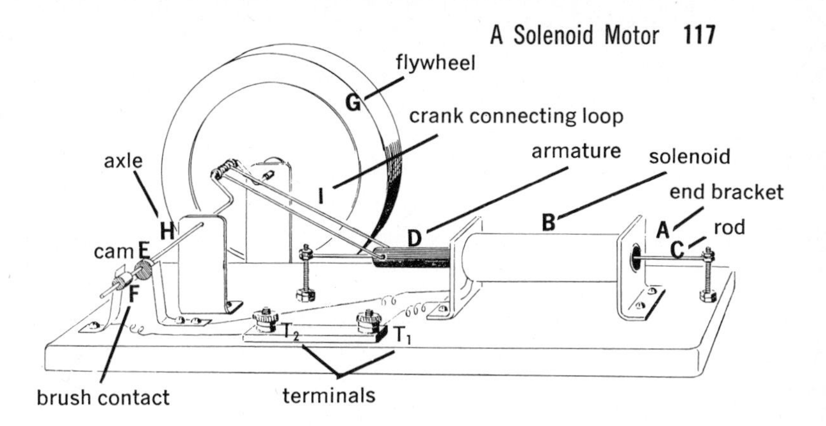

Fig. 45 Solenoid motor

is likely to be burned contacts. Oxidation is only satisfactorily avoided by the use of suitable contact metal such as is used in electric bell vibrators. Even a large-capacity condenser across the cam to brush gap does not appear to reduce the sparking there.

No great effort of imagination is needed to design, and it would be interesting to construct a double-acting specimen, the two pulls per revolution affording smoother action and higher speed.

The principle of a solenoid attracting an armature is widely employed. Many of us are familiar with the electromechanism by which car-light reflectors are dipped. A visit to the local telephone exchange will display a bewildering multiplicity of solenoids in action.

The field intensity in a long coil, in oersteds, is given by $\frac{4\pi ni}{10}$ where n is the number of turns per centimeter and i is the current in amperes.

The constant part $4\pi/10$ is about 1.26. But the important thing to remember is that this field, which effectively sucks in the core, depends on the product, amperes $\times$ turns.

22
A Simple Electric Motor

A rewarding exercise for the embryo electrician is to construct his own electric motor. If it is intended that the result is to be a power source for running large models, the motor will have to be well made, and made to orthodox dimensions. On the other hand, if it is merely to be an interesting demonstration model which will spin around at high speed, it may be much more loosely specified. The motor described here is capable of spinning color disks and driving light models when suitably geared down. It is of the two-pole armature form also known as Siemens or H-type. For this reason it is not necessarily self-starting, as a tripolar rotor would be.

Very briefly, the principle of this form of motor is as follows. A strong magnetic field is produced between the pole-pieces of a permanent or an electromagnet known as the field magnet. In the cylindrical gap between the poles spins a rotor called the armature. This also is an electromagnet which is capable of reversing polarity after each turn. The change of polarity, N-S-N-S-N . . . , is effected by reversal of the current in its windings, and the special switch which does this is called the commutator. The commutator is really the two bared ends of the armature winding mounted on a short tube of insulator built onto the same shaft. It is therefore in a fixed setting relative to the armature poles. Springing lightly against the commutator segments are two conductors called brushes, which feed the current into the armature coils. As rotation proceeds, it is clear that the ends of the coils are being made alternately positive and negative and, in our simple motor, this reversal occurs twice per revolution. We see that the actual pull on the armature, causing rotation, is magnetic attraction between its pole and the unlike field pole, assisted by the repulsion from the other like pole. The resulting twisting force, known to engineers as a torque or a couple, is not even in strength. It rises to a maximum twice a revolution but of course the momentum of the rotor smooths out the jerky effect even in this simple motor. A much more uniform torque is obtained in commercial multipole motors where the poles are in rapid succession being pulled up to the appropriate field-magnet pole. This is achieved by having a large number of windings and a correspondingly higher number of commutator segments. Even small motors such as those used in vacuum cleaners and power tools may have 22 commutator bars. They are designed to run on alternating current. D.C. motors are comparatively rare. The brushes in these motors are usually carbon rods pressed against the smooth commutator surface by light spiral springs. When they wear down as a result of friction and sparking they may have to be replaced and sometimes the commutator has also to be resurfaced in the lathe.

The component most likely to deter the constructor is the armature, and we therefore tackle this first.

In our case the following novel method of making an armature is adopted in order to avoid coping with the more usual plate laminations used to build up a core. Soft-iron wire is likely to be more readily obtainable than sheet iron, which so often in fact turns out to be mild steel sheet. This softness of the purer iron is a quality essential to the rapid reversal of magnetic flux which the core will have to undergo while spinning. The mild steel sheet of corrugated iron, car bodies, etc., is turned out in great quantities from modern steel rolling mills, but real iron is a rather scarce commodity. You will need some soft-iron wire about as thick as a pin. You may be able to get some from a florist. Obtain a couple of straight 4-in. iron nails, a straight steel knitting needle, and a block of wood. Referring to Fig. 46*a,* drill holes in the wood *I* at *B* and *D* to match the nails and at *F* to take the needle. These holes must be drilled perpendicular to the wood face and dead parallel. Scribe the circle *H* as shown in order to get the spacing precisely equal. It is advantageous to prepare the nails and the wire by first heating them to redness. This not only softens them mechanically but renders them more permeable to magnetism. Weave the soft-iron wire onto the nails as shown in diagram *a.* After several turns around the needle near *F,* continue the zigzag winding without distorting the nails, finishing with another tubular winding at G. Next, wrap on some cellophane tape to hold the arrangement rigid while sawing off the nails equal in length at the dotted lines near the wood block.

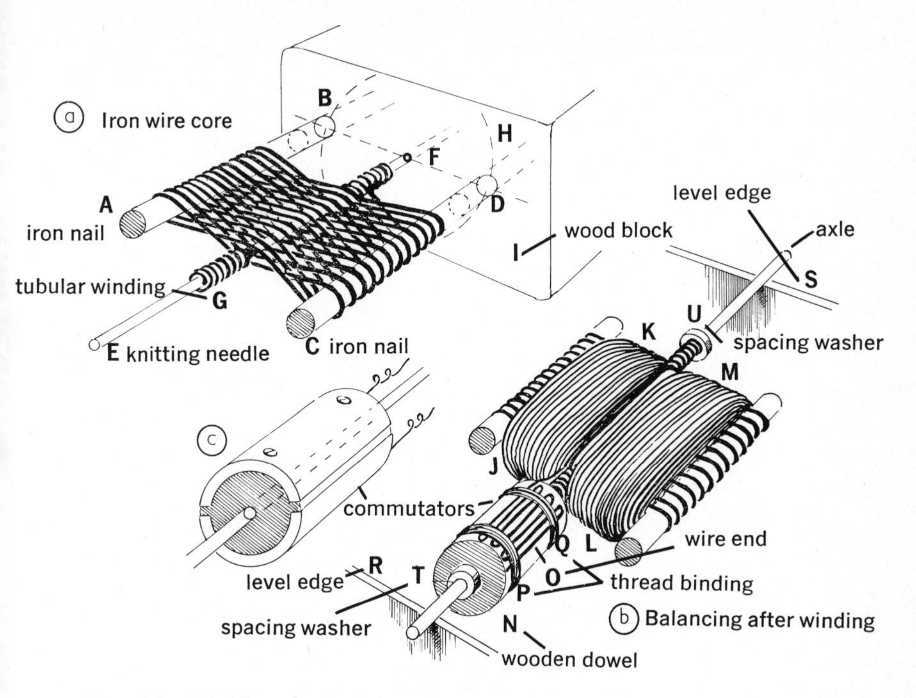

Fig. 46 Making the armature

As in Fig. 46*b,* make windings of insulated wire (A.W.G. 23), filling up the sides *JK* and *LM* with equal numbers of turns. Leave ends of wire some 6 in. long for construction of the commutator. Wrap on a further covering of cellophane tape to hold the wire in position and protect it.

A conventional commutator could be made as in Fig. 46*c* from a cylindrical Masonite core. This has a brass tube screwed on and is later segmented with two saw-cuts as shown, the ends of the coils being soldered to the halves. However, a simpler construction for the beginner is to make the free ends of the wire themselves act as segments. An inch or so of hardwood dowel rod, *N* in Fig. 46*b,* must be centrally drilled to grip the knitting-needle shaft. As the drill may drift, it may be necessary to true up the cylinder in the lathe. On each side of the rod zigzag the end of wire *O* and bind it down with thread at *P* and *Q*. Paint this over with Duco cement and, when dry, clean up the bare portion of the wires between *P* and *Q*. Spacing washers *T* and *U* may be necessary to fill up length between the bearings of the shaft.

At this stage it is best to balance the armature by resting it on level edges *R* and *S*. File off iron from the rod on the heavier side until the rotor shows no tendency to settle in one position.

The next operation is to make the field magnet. Obtain first a strip of iron about ⅛ in. thick, 1 in. wide, and some 8 in. long. Make sure that it is soft by heating it to bright redness in the fire and then cooling slowly. Bend it into the form shown by the black line *B* in Fig. 47*a*. Make it as symmetrical as possible and keep the curved portions real segments of circles. The radius in the gap should be just greater than the radius of the armature *A*, so that it can revolve there with as small a clearance as possible. Insulate the square part at the top with tape to protect the coil wire. Wind on some 200 turns of insulated wire *C* (A.W.G. 23) as neatly as possible, holding each layer in place with cellophane tape, until the top space is suitably filled up.

The brushes *E* and *F* can be ⅜-in. strips of springy metal (phosphor-bronze weather stripping) screwed down to the baseboard and pressing lightly against the commutator *D*. It may be convenient actually to screw them down with terminals, and additional screws by which the pressure may be adjusted are certainly an advantage. It should not be necessary to describe the construction of bearings for the armature shaft, but angle pieces of stout brass, *G* and *H*, may be drilled at a suitable level and firmly screwed down. In the absence of automatic oiling by oil-cups, it is essential to oil often,

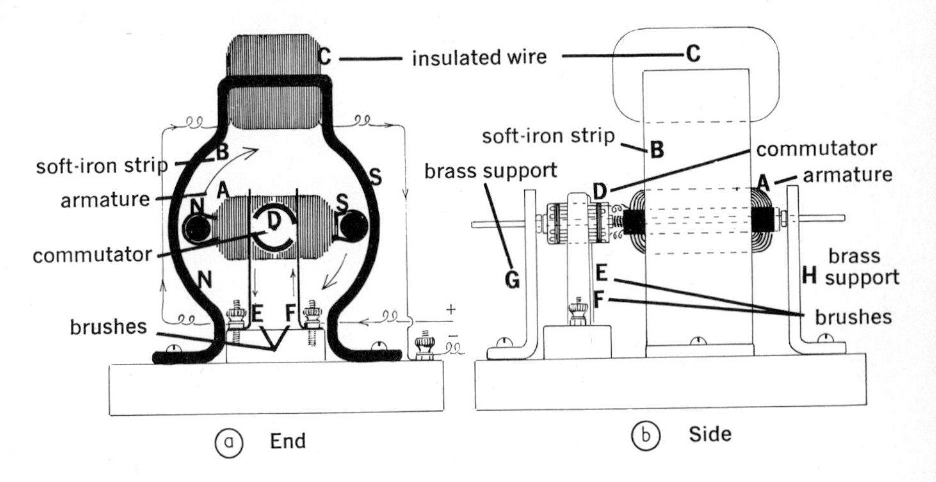

Fig. 47 Simple electric motor

as a dry bearing will quickly cause damage by cutting into the metal. Always make bearings from metals of two different degrees of hardness. Steel on steel or brass on brass is poor; steel on brass is good from the standpoint of smooth running.

Finally, terminals should be provided for connection of the battery. It will be seen that from the entrant terminal, current is fed to a brush, then passes through the rotor winding, through the other brush, in series through the field-magnet coil and so back to the battery. This is called a series-wound motor and illustrates the type of connection between field coils and armature winding used in most motors designed for variable-speed working, e.g., cranes, trains, and traction generally. Another mode of connection is to feed current simultaneously into the field coils and the brushes supplying the armature. This parallel sort of connection results in a shunt-wound motor, the type employed where steady speed is the requirement, e.g., in driving lathes.

The model now constructed should run vigorously

and at a high speed on a pressure of 6 to 12 volts. Oil the shaft bearings and smear a little grease on the commutator. There will be a best pressure for the springy brushes and also it may be better to rotate the commutator slightly relative to the armature. But these are matters for individual trial and error. Experiment should eventually give a very fast speed of rotation, the well-balanced rotor appearing as a mere blur.

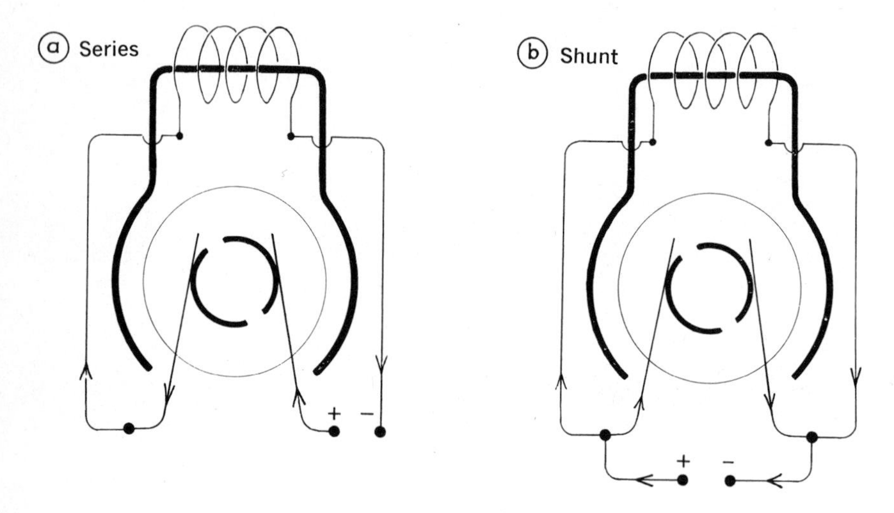

Fig. 48 Series and shunt winding compared

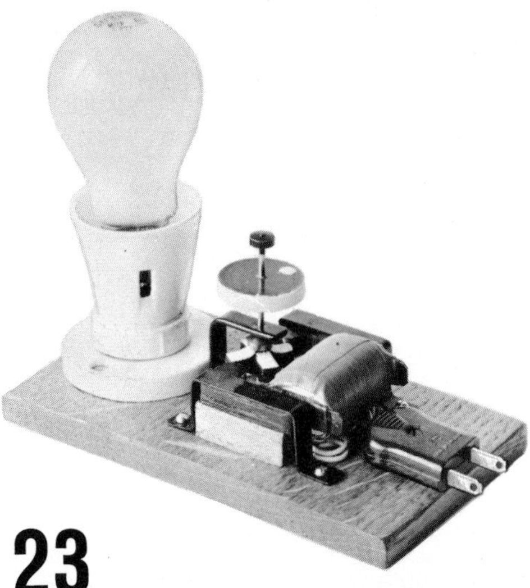

23
A Synchronous Wheel

Synchronous simply means keeping time. Many large organizations have one master clock controlling, throughout the building, a number of "slave" clocks which are simultaneously in step with the master timekeeper and are therefore said to be synchronous. The motor here described is little more than a spinning top but it clearly illustrates this principle of synchronism.

The actual rotor should be constructed in laminated form from a pile of strips of thin sheet iron ¼ in. wide by 1 in., each with a central ¹⁄₁₆-in. hole. These could be cut from the soft strip plentifully used in packaging crates nowadays, or the usual tin-can metal would serve. They are placed alternately to form a cross ¼ in. thick and wired in this position on a 3-in. steel knitting-needle axle while being soldered. Examine the plan and eleva-

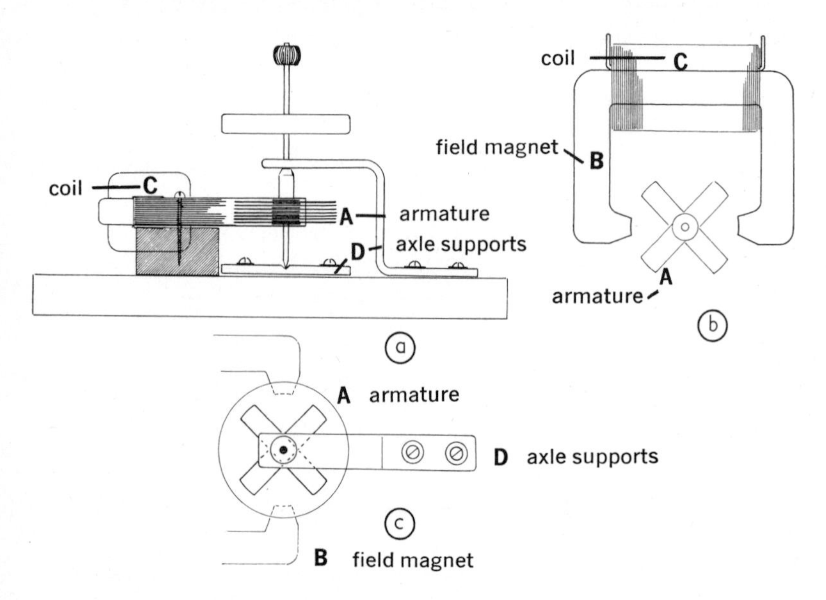

Fig. 49 The synchronous motor

tion in Fig. 49. The ends of the cross, the four teeth, are then neatly curved with a file to form the armature which will rotate between the poles of an A.C. field magnet. A 1¼-in. diameter flywheel of a fairly heavy material, such as Masonite, turned, drilled, and mounted friction-tight on the same axle, is advantageous.

Mark out on thick paper the shape of the field-magnet lamination shown at *B* in Fig. 49*b*, and stick it down on tinplate. Then with old scissors cut the shape out carefully so that it can be used as a template for two dozen or so. The number will be twice that of the strips in the armature. It is an advantage to paint them over with shellac, varnish, or any quick-drying paint before riveting them together with iron nail rivets. The long side of this iron core is insulated with tape and then wound with some 300 to 600 turns of thin wire about gauge 28. If the latter is the enameled magnet type, great care must be taken not to scrape the insulation accidentally, producing a short circuit in the coil *C* (Fig. 49*b*).

The axle supports, *D* in Fig. 49*a*, for the armature must next be made, from sheet brass preferably. The rotor may either spin like a top or on a horizontal axis, but in any case it should be carefully centralized and run very freely in oiled bearings. The whole is finally mounted on a base made of any available insulator, such as ebonite, Lucite, or Masonite. Terminals are fitted and the general appearance improved with enamel paint.

Alternating current is passed through the electromagnet. It may be taken either from the A.C. electricity in your house through an ordinary light bulb (40 to 100 watts) in series, or from a stepdown transformer giving 12 volts at 60-cycle frequency. Using house current, one must take the usual precautions to avoid danger and accidental short circuit. On spinning the wheel it should continue to rotate at a fixed speed, but several attempts may be needed.

The potential difference (P.D.) applied to the coil is fluctuating 60 times per second through maximum (+), zero, minimum (−) values and the current does likewise, though not quite in step with the voltage fluctuations. There are thus 120 large values of the current per second and therefore 120 magnetic tugs across the poles, which are, of course, reversing in polarity each time. On the four teeth this should result in 30 revolutions per second. Clearly, if the wheel is rotating at such a speed that the teeth lie nearly straight across the gap at each instant of pull, that speed will be maintained and any tendency to go faster or slower will be prevented. The speed is therefore constant and depends on the frequency of the supply. The wheel could, however, if spun sufficiently quickly at first, rotate at twice, or some low multiple of, this fixed number of revolutions. Try the effect of wrapping a linen thread around the spindle and pulling it off like a toy gyroscope cord to obtain this high initial multiple speed.

Paint a bright red spot on one tooth of the wheel so that it may be observed stroboscopically, a term needing a little explanation.

Repeated brief visual images of a repeated movement may give an impression of no movement at all provided they are synchronized with it. It is well known that the repeated images thrown at a fixed speed on the screen in the movies are fast enough for persistence of vision to give the impression of continuity. Now the spokes of a revolving wheel in the picture may appear in successive positions at this same speed and the wheel then appears stationary. A little slower rotation of the wheel and it appears to be revolving backward. On speeding up, the wheel appears to revolve faster, then slows down until at twice the speed it is again apparently stationary.

The repeated visual images may be produced either by viewing through a series of holes in a uniformly revolving plate, or by an intermittent illumination of the moving event. Such flickering illumination is readily available at 60 c.p.s. by making use of a neon lamp. There are 120 flashes per second, but since the light emitted is likely to be brighter for one direction of current than the other this may seem like 60. This rate of flashing is, in the normal way, too great to be apparent and the light looks continuous. With an ordinary filament bulb on A.C. the light is, of course, practically constant, since the filament has not had time to cool down between the current maxima.

If, then, we use the neon lamp as the source of illumination to examine the spinning synchronous wheel, it appears to be stationary. By switching off the A.C. supply to the wheel it appears to revolve backward in slowing down from its synchronous speed.

This type of fixed-speed wheel, with more teeth, is the motive power for A.C. electric clocks, a train of wheels simply stepping down the speed to 1 revolution per minute and 1 revolution per hour to carry the respective hands. Very simple in design, they will repay examination.

In the photograph on page 125 it will be seen that the bottom half of a 5-amp connector is attached to the apparatus while the socket half must be on the house-current wire. The reverse would be highly dangerous! The bulb is not a neon lamp but merely the current limiting resistance, a 40-watt filament bulb in series with the electromagnet winding.

24 A Generator of High Voltage

From the days of the experimenter Dr. William Gilbert, physician to the first Queen Elizabeth, electric sparks have always proved fascinating to inquiring minds. To give one example, about 1830 that great English pioneer of physics, James Prescott Joule, best known for his classical work on the mechanical equivalent of heat, made his first static electricity machine and Leyden jars before he was sixteen. We read that he and his brother entertained themselves by giving electric shocks to the family servants! Some thirty years later James Wimshurst gave further stimulus to the study of high-tension generation with his well-known induction machine, but the general attitude was that the inventions were merely toys, and interest in them waned until comparatively recently. However, a tremendous revival of interest followed the application of extremely high voltages to research on the fundamental particles of physics. In 1932, Cockcroft and Walton's linear accelerator was speeding up protons using pressures of hundreds of thousands of volts and the era of the atom-smasher had arrived. Essential tools of modern nuclear research are generators of enormously high electrical pressures, the synchrotrons, bevatrons, and other high-sounding successors which can produce energy beams at billions of electron-volts.

One of the earliest forms of high-potential generator to prove useful in this respect was Van de Graaff's machine in Chicago (1933), a recent example of which gives an energy output stepped up to 12 million electron-volts. For insulation purposes the latter works in a pressurized container which is some 45 ft. high.

Reverting now to a scale more within our scope we shall describe the making of a little model working on the same Van de Graaff principle.

Basically, the action of the machine is extremly simple. Charge sprayed from points onto a moving pulley-band made of some good insulator such as silk is carried up to a large top prime conductor. There it is transferred to the outer surface and the potential of this large ball rises to a limit set merely by its size and by the leakage rate. If the leakage is greater than the charging rate, then naturally the conductor will never charge up at all. Hence the essence of good construction lies in avoidance of leakage (good insulation) and large electrostatic capacity (large size). It must be assumed that the reader knows enough of electrostatics to appreciate the discharging effect of sharp edges and points and also the principle of induction of opposite charge in a neighboring surface when electrolines run across from a charge on a conductor. As this is essential to understanding the build-up of charge on the top conductor of our model, we shall note down these fundamental ideas:

i. Charge always resides on the *surface* of a hollow conductor.

ii. The density of charge is not evenly spread over the outside of a conductor of varying surface curvature. It is greatest where the curvature is greatest and rises to a very high concentration on any sharp projection, but it is small where the surface is flatter—hence the bulky smoothness of the top ball.

iii. Like charges repel each other and therefore work must be done in pushing them together (positively charged belt approaching positively charged sphere). Conversely, unlike charges, which attract, as on the positive sphere and the departing belt carrying its induced negative charge, will need input of work to pull them apart. This work, done in mechanically revolving the belt against electrostatic forces, and conceived as stretching the electrolines, is the real source of the electrical energy ultimately stored in the charged machine.

It is even more advisable than usual to assemble the required parts before attempting the construction of this model, as some of the pieces may not be readily available from the scrap box. Alternative and perhaps better ideas for sources of material may occur to the reader but we shall here describe the author's model as it was made.

In the first place the prime conductor, *A* in Fig. 50, was made from two aluminum bowls linked together into a round-ended cylinder with aluminum sheet. The bowls were 6½ in. in diameter. Spherical shape would be just

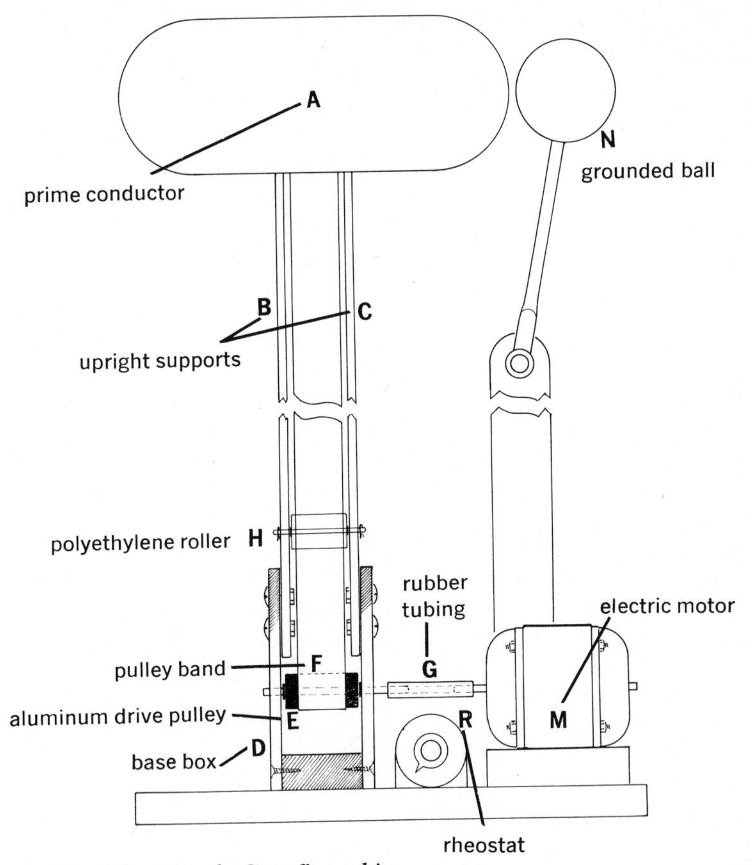

Fig. 50 Van de Graaff machine

as suitable but the form adopted was constructionally easier. In any case it is vital to have the surface smooth and polished. The bowls had their flat bases pushed and beaten out on a leather sandbag into hemispherical form. They were then linked to a curve of aluminum sheet (see Fig. 51*a*), using a proprietary aluminum metal solder (really an adhesive). This was finished off with file and emery and finally shellac-varnished over the jointing.

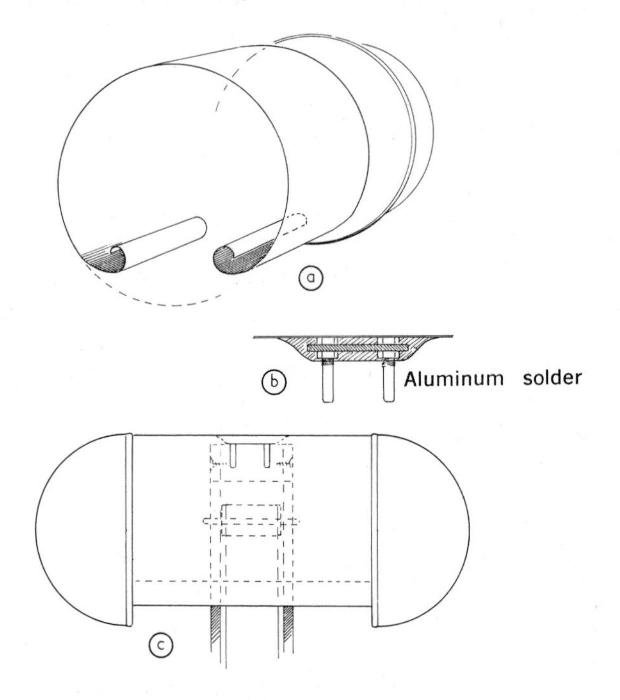

Fig. 51 Details of Van de Graaff machine

No external attachment fittings or projections are allowable in supporting the globe on its insulators and so two bolts were rigidly fixed to the inside top, as shown in Fig. 51*b*, again by means of a heavy layer of the aluminum solder. The bolts were first spaced by a plate as shown and had most of the thread turned off. The pins so formed could drop into matching holes in the top cross-piece of the vertical frame.

Next, the upright supports, *B* and *C* in Fig. 50, were made from a pair of strips of polyethylene 2 in. broad by 27 in. long and ⅜ in. thick, especially purchased for electrostatic work. As the surface normally remains dry, polyethylene makes an ideal insulator. Possibly Lucite strips of thinner gauge would serve almost as well here, but the Masonite uprights first tried by the writer were found to have too great a surface leakage. The verticals were held 2½ in. apart by off-cuts of the strip, forming an open-sided box, and in fact the joints were made by blowpipe melting of the polyethylene itself, with scrap polyethylene as the jointing glue. The lower end of this frame was vertically slotted to take screws by which it was clamped to a rigid base box, *D* in Fig. 50, in which the lower drive pulley *E* ran. Made adjustable in this way, it could be raised if necessary to take up stretch in the pulley-band *F* and also tilted slightly if the belt showed a tendency to run to one side. Note that belts run toward the tighter side, hence the doming of pulleys to keep the belt in the middle.

Two kinds of cylindrical pulley were required for the apparatus, one of metal and one of insulator. For the metal ones the writer was able to make use of scrapped 2-μF condenser cases which happened to be aluminum cylinders of the right size, but these pulleys could be built up from tubing. Again, the insulating rollers were conveniently made from small polyethylene bottles. The necks were cut off, brass rods centralized through the bottles, and the space filled up with a setting wax. Extra care was taken in making the spindles through the metal cylinders perfectly central. Of these, the lower one formed the drive roller and here the rod was rigid with the cylinder and long enough to project an inch or so beyond the upright side plate. This roller was driven by being joined by a short length of rubber pressure-tubing *G* to the shaft of an electric motor *M*, rheostat-controlled for speed *R*. There is, of course, no reason why the belt should not be driven by a handle, geared up for speed by a wheel and pinion from an Erector set or by a simple pulley-drive.

As to the belt itself, thin rubber was found to work

well until the inequality at the joint caused failure there. It was eventually replaced by a 2-in. strip of plastic curtain material (polyethylene) joined with plastic cement. This was found to last under strenuous running conditions. It is interesting to test the electrostatic quality of the plastic curtain material by holding two narrow strips in one hand and charging them simply by running the other hand down them. The like frictional charges so acquired cause them to stand apart, as in a charged pith-ball electroscope, and leakage is very slow indeed.

Transfer of charge to and from the belt can be by means of a row of sharp points, *C* in Fig. 52, or by means of blades. In the writer's model, tubes were drilled to take rows of phonograph needles, but doubtless a sharpened edge of metal strip would work as well. The points should just clear the racing band of plastic; otherwise, disastrous consequences ensue!

A simplified explanation of the electrical operation of the machine, which Fig. 52 will clarify, is as follows: Some inequality of charge distribution, due perhaps to friction with the lower plastic roller, causes positive charge to jump the small gap from the lower-lefthand comb to the belt. It is carried up on this "moving-staircase" and picked off by the point action of the upper comb. Once inside the dome it is instantly transferred to the outer face. Now, as the belt is pulled down on the right it acquires by induction a negative charge as it leaves the positive dome. The polyethylene rollers bring the two sides of the belt close together, and the descending negative induces more positive on the ascending left side. Meanwhile, the negative on the belt pulls off a stream of positive charge from the lower combs, supplied from the ground, and thus we have a sort of compound-interest effect, more and more positive charge piling up

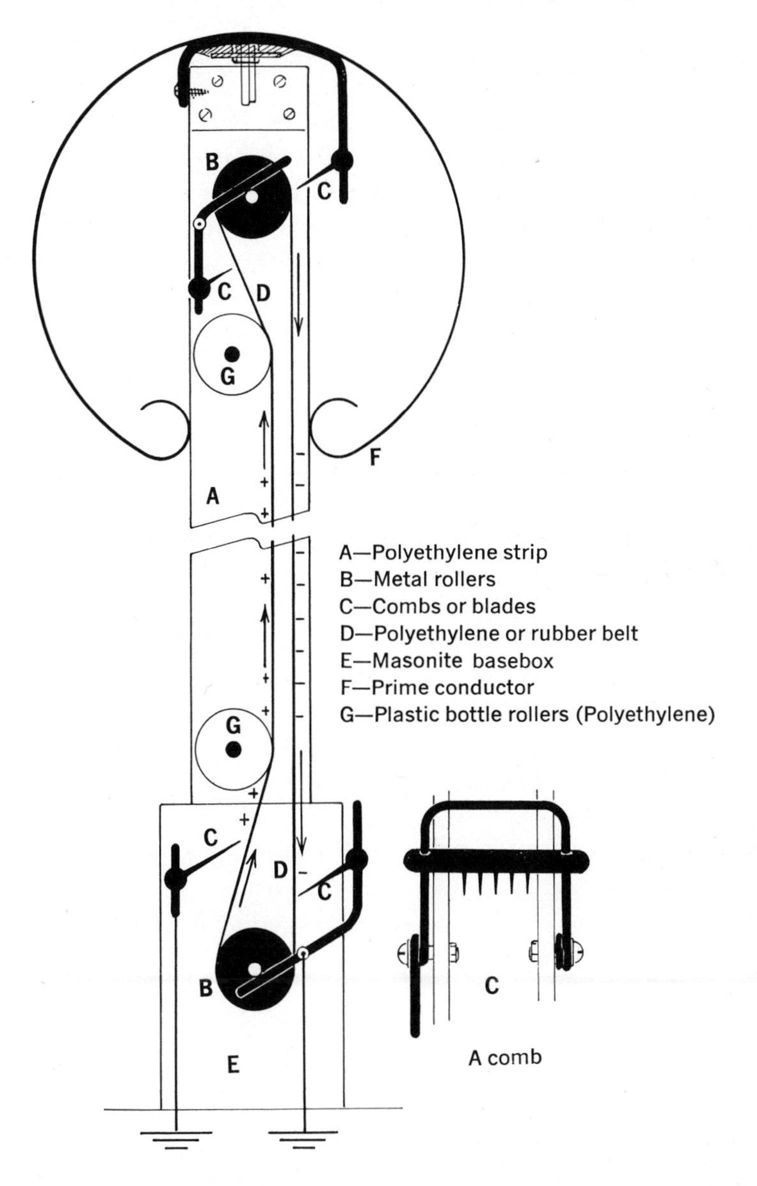

Fig. 52 Van de Graaff (not to scale)

on the dome. With the machine working in the dark, the corona or brush-discharge from the lower combs may be clearly seen. The principle of charge acquisition would be the same, were positive or negative accumulated on the dome; indeed, change of belt material to silk or even accidental initial conditions might result in reversal of all the charge signs marked on the diagram.

In good conditions, i.e., dry and dust free, sparks several centimeters long should jump to the adjustable grounded ball, *N* in Fig. 50. This conductor was made by sticking tinfoil onto a large wooden ball mounted on a hinged metal tube as shown. In the machine described here, the actual discharge combs near the plastic tape could slide on heavy-gauge copper wire pivoted so that their tail ends rested against the metal roller spindles. They were thus adjustable for relative position and this was found to control to some extent the efficiency of working.

Without Leyden jars attached, sparks from the machine are harmless, giving little more than a slight prickling shock. Tissue-paper strips, or silk threads made into a tassel, stand apart amusingly when attached to the charged dome and appear to grasp an approaching finger. A point of metal attached will almost blow out a candle flame by its associated draft of particles as the charge streams away. Many other such experiments, which space precludes describing, may in fact be performed.

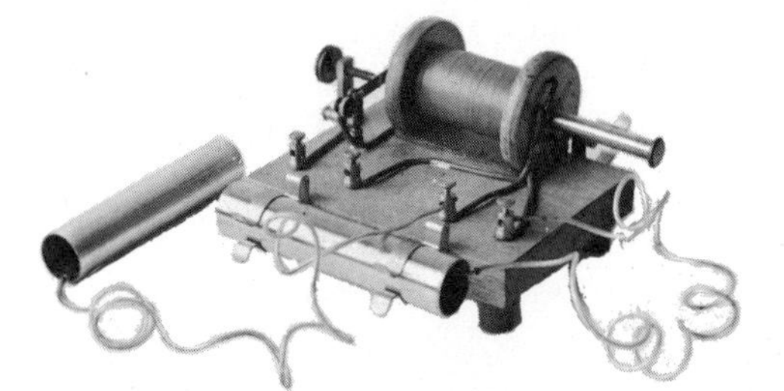

25 An Induction or Shocking Coil

You may wish to construct a small induction or shocking coil which is at once harmless, very instructive, and a good source of fun. Before embarking on its making we would do well to consider its scientific basis. It is a form of transformer developing very high output voltages from a low input voltage.

Sometimes in physics we may be misled into thinking that we are getting some energy for nothing. This in fact would be a prerequisite of the various perpetual motion devices suggested from time to time (which never work!). For example, a machine which lifts a heavy load by application of a much smaller force, as in a lever or a jack or a hydraulic lift, may give this erroneous impression. Actually, what is gained in the force ratio, the mechanical advantage, is more than lost in the relative distances moved. Now, in the transformer we have a somewhat analogous electrical state of affairs. It builds up a bigger output pressure (voltage) but only at the cost of giving a smaller current (amperage), and on balance the output of power (amperage times voltage) is always rather less than the input. Nevertheless, this discovery by Faraday has proved to be one of our most useful devices.

In its simplest form a transformer consists of two insulated coils, *P* and *S* in Fig. 53*a,* through which passes a soft-iron core *C,* thereby linking their magnetic fields. In order to be more susceptible to magnetic change the core is usually laminated, i.e., built up from a pile of plates. The coils may be on separate bobbins as in Fig. 53*a,* or even overlapped on the same core as in Fig. 53*b,* as long as the magnetic field of coil *P* also penetrates coil *S,* though the latter straight-core arrangement would be much less efficient. Voltages are induced in the secondary coil *S* whenever current in the primary coil *P* changes, but as long as only steady current flows in *P* no current can be detected in S.

The supply in *P* must therefore be either fluctuating in strength, or starting and stopping (intermittent), or constantly reversing in direction (alternating), before any effect is obtained in coil *S.* Ordinary transformers have an A.C. input, hence an A.C. output (often at the common frequency of 60 cycles per second). It must be realized that coils *P* and *S* are completely insulated from each other and also that their number of turns is usually vastly different. The point is that the output pressure is greater than the input pressure, in the ratio of the number of turns on the secondary to the number of turns on the primary coil. That is to say that the voltage is stepped-up although the amperage is proportionately stepped-down. Chapter 26 describes in further detail the

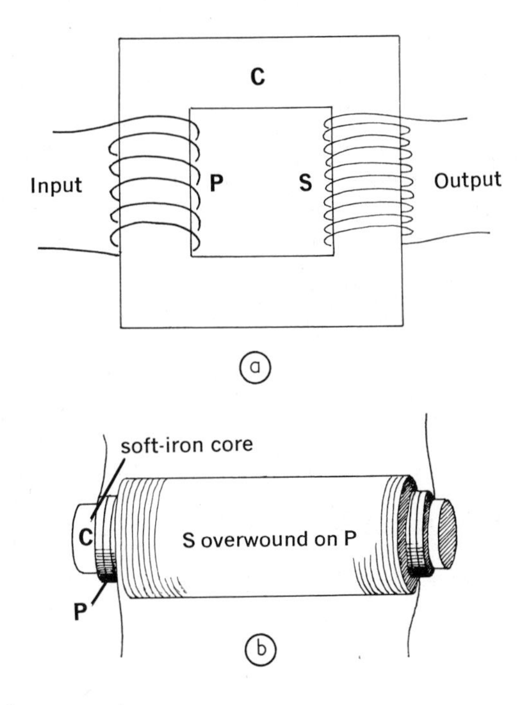

Fig. 53 Transformer action

interaction between transformer coils. In that case the electromagnetic linkage between the two coils will be seen to be variable in degree, but in the design of most transformers the coupling is fixed.

Basically, then, our induction coil is to be a kind of step-up transformer designed to increase the voltage of a 4½-volt flashlight battery perhaps to the shocking figure of 270 volts. This would require a turns-ratio on *P* and *S* of 1:60, or 50 turns to 3,000 turns. The flashlight battery gives direct current but we may render it intermittent, making and breaking at quite a high speed by the same simple device used in the electric bell. This buzzer action will start and stop the current in the pri-

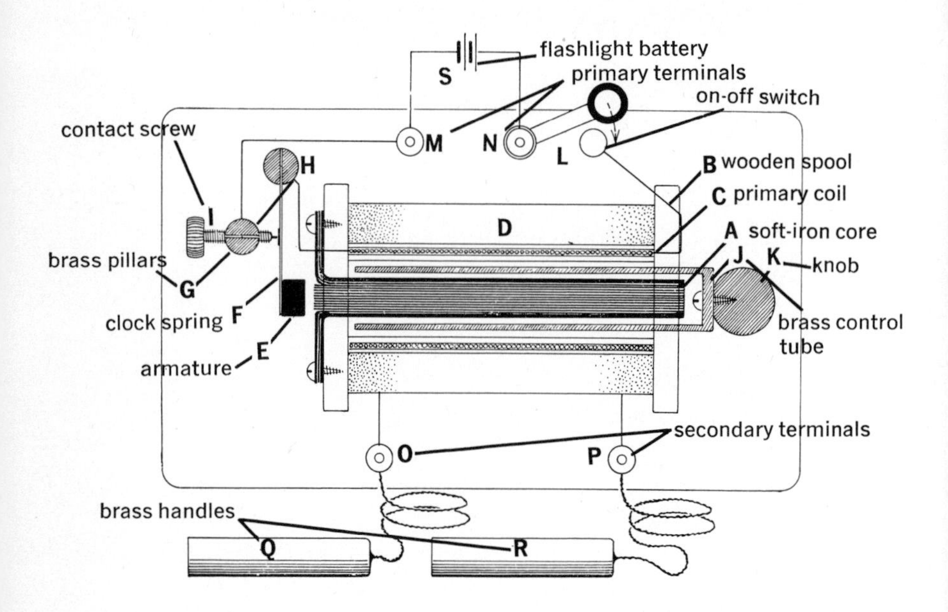

Fig. 54 Shocking coil

mary coil. The number of turns in the secondary coil, overlaid on the primary, is not at all critical, but obviously it will have to be very fine wire to wind the high number of turns, and well insulated to stand the high voltage. The primary wire can be much thicker.

A further requirement will clearly be some controlling device which will limit the voltage and the degree of shock taken from the secondary-coil terminals.

Fig. 54 shows the general layout of the apparatus, and since the sizes are not at all critical no dimensions are given, but in fact spool *B* was about 4½ in. long. This is an empty reel of wire but it could be made up very simply from a tube of cardboard with thick, rigidly fixed end-plates. The inner rod *A* was a core of soft iron, laminated insofar as it was made from soft-iron wire.

This wire was wrapped first into a flat coil, twisted up into a rod, and then one end spread into two wings. These were screwed on to one end-plate of the reel *B*. The core *A* was trimmed up cylindrically and to some degree solidified by soldering the surface as a matter of convenience, though this partly defeats the object of the lamination, reduction of eddy currents. The core was in any case made smaller than the hole in *B* so that a brass tube *J* could form an adjustable sliding sleeve on it. We shall return to the purpose of this tube later.

The first winding on *B* was the primary coil *C*, which was 50 turns of D.C.C. copper wire (A.W.G. 19). Its ends were brought out to the primary terminals *MN* through an on-off switch *L*. As the primary windings would be quite inaccessible once the upper layers were wound, its ends had been soldered to twisted double wire with separate insulation on each strand in case of accidental breakage. The primary winding was covered with a layer of paraffined paper held in place with cellophane tape. Then the secondary coil was overwound on this level surface. This coil consisted of some 3,000 turns of much thinner wire (A.W.G. 28) and, as each layer was wound, a facing of waxed paper was overlaid. This kept the layers flat and neat as well as providing necessary insulation. Again the coil was finished off with twisted double wire with separate insulation on each strand to avoid damage to the easily cracked single strand of fine wire, and this led to a couple of well-insulated terminals *O* and *P*. The winding of the secondary was in fact done with the aid of a geared spindle with a cyclometer counter attached. Winding 3,000 turns is not a very tedious operation and the exact number of turns is immaterial, but the geared winder saves time.

The make-and-break of the primary, being essentially

similar to that of an electric bell, could probably be made up from available scrap metal. *G* and *H* were two short brass pillars screwed into the baseboard. The pillar *H* rigidly held one end of a piece of clock spring *F*, with a small soft-iron armature *E* attached. *G* was a slotted and tapped post which gripped the adjustable contact screw *I*. The screw was tipped with nonoxidizable metal and the spring *F* similarly faced with it since this avoided burned-contact trouble associated with sparking. The rate of buzzing of the vibrator had to be high and this rate was determined by two factors. First, the spring was fairly stiff and, second, the soft-iron load was not too massive. The primary circuit, energized by a 4½-volt battery, is seen to be quite isolated from the secondary but is, of course, linked inductively.

Brass tubes *Q* and *R*, each soldered to a 2-ft length of insulated wire, formed handles attached to the secondary terminals. When not in use they were held in spring metal clips screwed to the sides of the baseboard.

Assuming that the above construction has been carried out, operation of the apparatus presents no difficulty. With the vibrator *EF* buzzing smoothly and fast, the control tube J is fully pushed in by the insulated knob *K* to obtain minimum output. In this position, the handles are firmly grasped with *dry* hands and the controller is gradually drawn out to give the required degree of shock. Note that the bearable limit varies with different persons and with the degree of dryness of the hands, i.e., with body resistance. It is therefore very unpleasant and unwise to pick up the handles while K is in the out position. The experience of a few nasty shocks is salutary and will soon emphasize this warning against careless use.

It is interesting to speculate on how the brass control tube limits the output potential. While the metal tube is fully inserted, heavy eddy currents are generated in it. These will always be in such a direction (by Lenz's Law) as to oppose the build-up of magnetic field. Induced voltages in the secondary are therefore limited and the shock is negligible. Electrical conduction in the core itself, e.g., by soldering of the laminations, would have similar reducing effect. We must not fall into the error of picturing the metal sleeve cutting off the magnetic field of the core as it slides onto it; brass, of course, is non-magnetic and would not do this.

Having made the shocking coil as a toy, the reader will probably like to follow up his experiments with further reading on how large practical spark coils are constructed. This will show the vital necessity of high insulation between the so-called pies or slabs of secondary coil, and also the use of a big capacity condenser to reduce sparking at the vibrator contacts.

One widespread application of the induction coil—never envisaged by Ruhmkorff, after whom it is often named—is in our present car-ignition systems. At one time medical X-ray apparatus and other discharge tubes made wide use of Ruhmkorff coils as the source of high tension, but nowadays they are usually superseded by other types of transformer.

26
A Variable Transformer

The young electrician quickly comes up against the need for a direct-current source more effective than the flashlight batteries usual to his early experiments with circuits and lamps.

It is therefore suggested that useful models to construct quite early are a house-current transformer giving variable output at a lower and safer voltage than the usual 110 volts, say maximum 30 volts A.C., and a rectifier for converting this to D.C. even if it is not well smoothed. One can then at least experiment with D.C. motors, electrolysis, accumulator charging, and so on, without the annoyance of finding the battery supply failing or inadequate for the purpose required.

The apparatus described here will not have the high-percentage efficiency of the manufacturers' product—

actually a point of little importance—but offsetting this is the advantage that its construction and action will be thoroughly understood by the builder.

Commercial transformer stampings are of special soft iron of high permeability, but if this cannot be obtained, ordinary iron sheet may be utilized, with an accompanying loss in efficiency.

We must first be clear about the general principle involved. Fluctuating current at high voltage from house current is fed through a coil of a large number of turns mounted on a laminated iron core or ring. The resulting flux or magnetic field, reversing as it does at 60 cycles per second in this core, produces an induced electromotive force in a secondary coil. This may have one-eighth the number of turns of the primary coil and is wound on the same core. Induced alternating current can therefore be taken from the secondary winding, dependent in magnitude, of course, on the resistance of the output circuit. Now, the electromotive force is stepped down in the same ratio of reduction as the turns on the secondary to those on the primary, so that if the input is at a root mean square voltage of 120, the output electromotive force may be one-eighth, or 15 volts. The effectiveness of this transfer of energy depends on the magnetic coupling between the coils. This is naturally greatest if the windings are closely adjacent and parallel and if the ring of core iron is complete. Our variable transformer will allow for the separation of the coils and breaking the magnetic ring to the desired degree by slider adjustment.

Before attempting the model shown in Fig. 56, you would be well advised to study induction and transformer action from any electricity book.

First cut a thin cardboard template the shape and size of the core laminations, as shown at each *A* in Fig. 55*a*. This

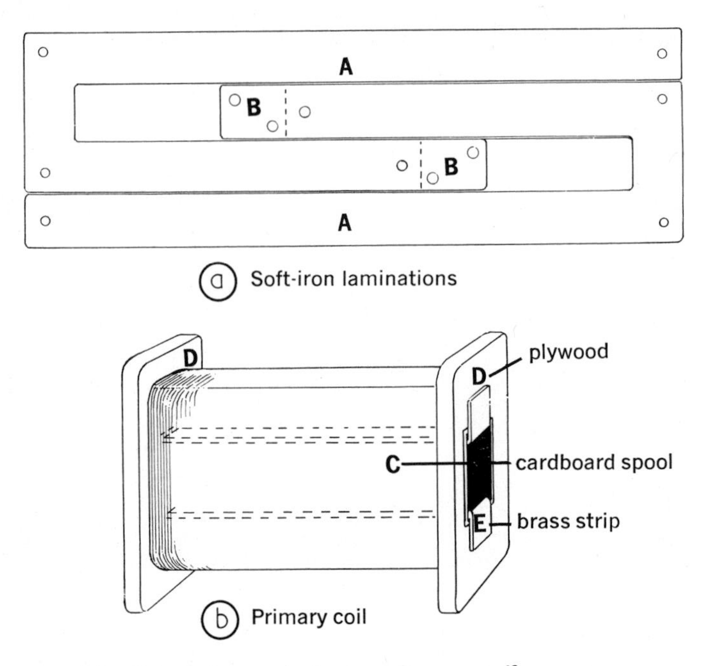

Fig. 55 Laminations and a transformer coil

is for marking out U-shaped ¾-in. strips of sheet iron 10 in. by 2½ in. To save wastage in cutting, the pieces are economically interlocked as shown and they may be cut out with snips or old garden shears. If this cutting of awkward shapes proves to be too tedious it is possible to build up a similar core from straight strips. After being flattened, the plates are coated with shellac varnish and riveted together with iron nails. Two close rivets are put in the last ¾ in., *B*, as this is to be sawed off the main core and used as a slider.

For the primary coil, a cardboard spool, *C* in Fig. 55*b*, with glued-on plywood ends *DD*, is constructed to fit the iron core section. Inserted strips of brass *E*, bent over the ends, will prevent these being pulled off during the winding of the coil. With a little ingenuity one can easily make some form of winder to rotate this spool while the wire is being wrapped. Wind on some 1,200 turns of gauge 25 D.C.C. wire as neatly and closely as possible, overlaying with gummed paper strip or cellophane tape every few layers.

The secondary spool *S* in Fig. 56 is shorter but carries thicker wire. It is made similarly but wound with 150 turns of gauge 21 wire. The hole through this spool must be large enough for it to slide smoothly on the shorter arm of the iron core. The small block of laminations *B* is strapped onto the end-plate of this coil *S* and slides in the gap between the arms to form a closed magnetic ring when fully inserted.

As shown in the perspective sketch of Fig. 56, the coil *S* and the attached block *B* may be withdrawn by the rod *C* and knob *D*. C passes through an end-plate on the apparatus and may be clamped at any desired position by means of a set-screw *I*. Insulated wire from the movable secondary coil *S* leads to the output terminal sockets *G* and *H*. The input leads, also of insulated wire,

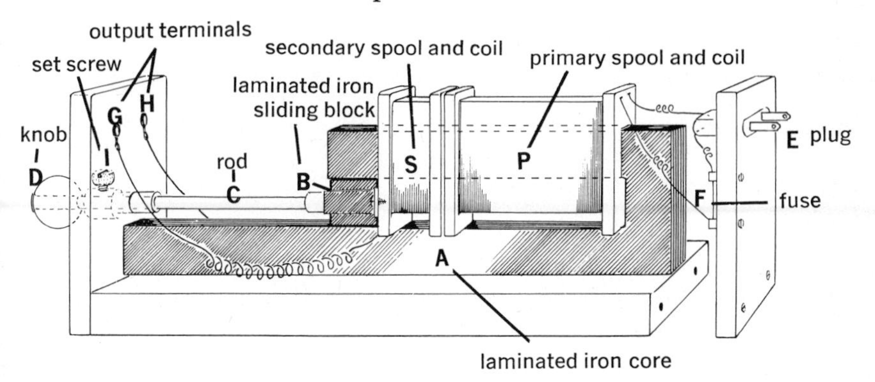

Fig. 56 Variable transformer (casing removed and right-hand end detached)

link the 5-amp plug *E* with the primary coil *P* through a 5-amp fuse *F*, these leads being well insulated with plastic sleeving. For obvious safety reasons the socket part of the connector *E* is on the supply side of the cable from the house current and the plug is on the apparatus itself.

In the model shown in the photograph an A.C. ammeter has been inserted in one of the output leads and there are other minor differences from the drawn design of Fig. 56. The photographed model gives a pressure range up to 20 volts root mean square which falls off as the load is increased up to 4-amp root mean square. Its chief fault is that with continuous running the iron core becomes too hot to handle, but the apparatus is very serviceable for short periods of use.

This defect would probably be eliminated if stampings of the correct quality iron were employed. The core loss would be greatly reduced. Another minor disadvantage in use is the noise made by the vibration. The noise has been lessened by making the block *B* a good fit, graphite-greased for sliding, between the arms of *A*. Rubber feet on the baseboard and use of the clamping screw on the slider rod also help to reduce the noise. Pushing in the slider knob increases the output current, since this is determined by the degree of coupling, and the apparatus gives a very smoothly adjustable current.

In the next two chapters of the book we indicate how current output may also be resistance-controlled and how the A.C. from the transformer may be converted into the D.C. needed for motors, electrolysis, and so on.

27 Direct-Current Supply and Control

When one has constructed a motor or any piece of electrical apparatus it is often convenient, and sometimes necessary, to be able to control the supply of current to it. The current is measured with an ammeter of suitable range. Although both direct and alternating current may be controlled by inclusion of variable resistance in the circuit, A.C. is often regulated by variable transformers and chokes.

Let us look first at the simpler matter of direct current. It is assumed that this comes from a storage battery. Any such supply to a lamp or an electromagnet or a motor may be controlled by altering the opposition to flow of current. The variable resistance which does this is called a rheostat and this simply consists of a coil of suitable bare resistance wire with a terminal at one end and a sliding contact on the wire, Fig. 57*a*. The part *U* is unused at the moment and therefore does not affect the circuit, but the part *R* limits the current, and when increased in length, further reduces the current flowing.

A rheostat is not difficult to make. Even thin iron or

steel wire could be used for resistance, e.g., the spiral wire used for spring curtain rods. It may not be quite so effective as the conventional alloys used, manganin or constantan, but is probably more easily obtainable. Detailed instructions are superfluous here, but a control resistance can very simply be made up by attaching the steel curtain spring, zigzag fashion, to an insulating board, or by wrapping it around a slate (see Fig. 57*b*). The wire should be permanently stretched until the coils are just separated. An alligator clip *C* makes a good movable contact and the ends of the wire can be clamped under terminals *A* and *B*. Bare curtain wire of the type mentioned was tested by the writer and found to have a resistance of 0·84 ohms per ft. of slightly stretched spring. It became too hot to handle at 3 amp and scorched paper when passing 4½ amp. The limit, red heat, depended on the ventilation draught past the wire, but was in the region of 9 amp. If the maximum resistance desired is known, calculation of the required length is clearly an easy matter.

Simple electrical calculations are very important and from the earliest stages an electrician should become familiar with the basic law connecting pressure and resistance and resulting current.

Briefly, this law, Ohm's Law, is that for any circuit or for any part of a circuit

$$\text{Current} = \frac{\text{Pressure drop}}{\text{Resistance}}$$

or, in the units used for measuring these quantities,

$$\text{Amperes} = \frac{\text{Volts}}{\text{Ohms}} \qquad \text{Symbolically, } I = \frac{E}{R}$$

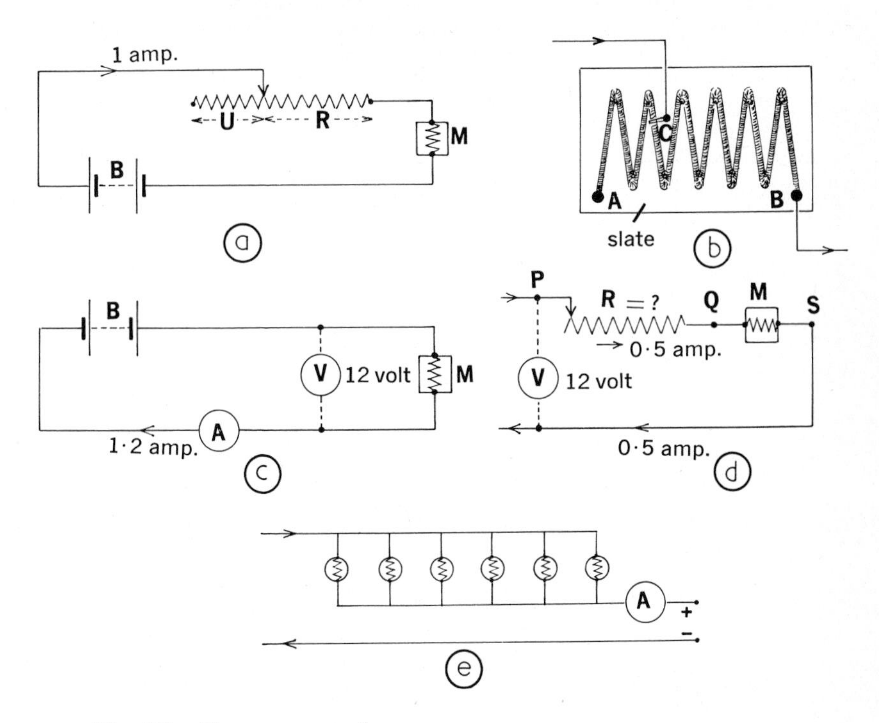

Fig. 57 Current control

The rule enables us to find any one of the three terms, given the other two. An example with easy figures may make this clear:

Example. If a car dashboard bulb to be used on a 12-volt battery is designed to carry 0·5 amp, what is the resistance of its filament?

Let the required resistance $= R$ ohms

$$I = 0{\cdot}5 \text{ amp}$$
$$E = 12 \text{ volts}$$
$$I = \frac{E}{R} \therefore 0{\cdot}5 = \frac{12}{R} \therefore 0{\cdot}5\,R = 12$$
$$R = 24 \text{ ohms}$$

A further type of calculation which the experimenter is likely to need, the estimation of a rheostat value, is shown below:

Example. Suppose, in the circuit Fig. 57*c*, the motor M is supplied from the battery B and the ammeter A reads 1·2 amp while the voltmeter V reads 12 volts.

Since $I = \frac{E}{R}$ $R = \frac{E}{I}$

$\therefore$ Resistance of motor = 10 ohms

What, then, would one make the maximum resistance of a rheostat which would cut down the current through the motor to half an ampere?

Referring to Fig. 57*d*:

Let E volts be the pressure drop across the motor itself.

Applying Ohm's Law (in the form $E = IR$) to the motor,

$$E = 0{\cdot}5 \times 10$$
$$= 5 \text{ volts}$$

Of the total 12-volt drop across PS a drop of 5 volts occurs in the motor QS, thus the remaining 7-volt drop must be in the rheostat PQ.

Apply Ohm's Law (in the form $R = \frac{E}{I}$) to PQ.

Let R be the rheostat resistance:

$I = 0{\cdot}5$ amp as in the rest of the circuit

$E = 7$ volts

$\therefore R = \frac{7}{0{\cdot}5}$ $\therefore R = 14$ ohms

Thus a maximum value of 14 ohms would be required to cut the current through the motor to ½ amp.

One might notice, incidentally, that

$$\frac{\text{Resistance of } R}{\text{Resistance of } M} = \frac{\text{Volts drop across } R}{\text{Volts drop across } M}$$

which is a way of expressing the proportionality that exists between resistance and fall of voltage throughout a circuit.

Control of current by a rheostat always involves wastage of energy in the control resistance itself. This is a further consideration in selecting *R*, because the energy wasted there is converted into heat. The rheostat must be designed not only to pass the requisite current but also to dissipate the heat generated. The product of the current and voltage-drop across the rheostat is the rate of energy consumption there, in units called watts, and this determines the quantity of heat generated. In fact the resistance must not only have the correct ohmic value, but must be capable of carrying the correct wattage without undue heating up. Overheated, it could fuse or be a source of danger.

One form of variable resistor which the amateur can readily build up consists of a group of parallel lamps. Such a "lamp-bank" is sometimes employed in supplying the correct current to accumulators being charged. In this instance the wastage of heat energy is obvious enough. As shown in Fig. 57*e*, the lamps may be plugged into a group of sockets wired in parallel on a baseboard, and the more lamps inserted, the bigger the current through the ammeter *A*.

Another method of heavy current limitation makes use of the resistance of a liquid conductor, such as a

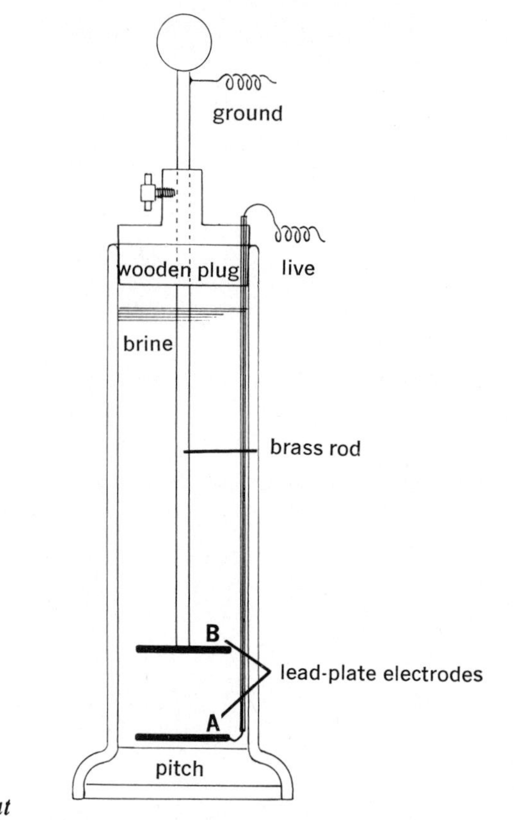

Fig. 58
Liquid rheostat

strong salt solution. Used in the past as an emergency dimmer for theater lights, this device is nowadays usually replaced by conventional wire rheostats. Fig. 58 shows a cylinder such as a small drainpipe sealed at the bottom and filled with strong brine. *A* and *B* are two lead-plate electrodes. Current enters at the lower disk *A* by way of the insulated wire and leaves through the brass rod of the adjustable upper disk *B*. The latter can be clamped at a height appropriate to the degree of dimming required and when *B* actually touches *A* the lights are fully on.

Raising B increases the resistance of the tank and dims the lights. This is a cheap form of controller, but it need hardly be stressed that when used with house current a vital necessity for safety is adequate insulation of all parts handled.

28
On Rectifiers

Familiarity with the rather complex control systems of electric-train circuits may acquaint a boy with voltage-dropping transformers and rectifiers, but he is naturally very hazy about the scientific principles involved. The schoolboy's approach to electricity follows a fairly common pattern. Usually before the age of ten he has with more or less success dismembered and reassembled his flashlight. He puts colored paper or gelatin in front of the bulb. He observes the necessity for good contacts and circuit completion. By extension of wiring from his battery he enjoys flashing bulbs on and off from a distant switching point. But long before experimentation is finished, he is in the sad position of owning an exhausted battery giving but a depressingly dim glow in the bulbs. Worse still, when he wishes to run little electric motors, electromagnetic relays, etc., even a storage battery will not stand up to the strain. That spare or ancient battery from father's car is always strangely devoid of life and energy. The answer to this lies in the battery charger itself, complete with safety fuses, a house-current–derived source of direct current. Fairly cheap models giving about 3-amp output are now on the market even in the department stores, but more satisfaction would lie in building one's own unit. Combining the transformer of the previous section with a homemade rectifier is feasible, though it should be stated at the outset that the purchase of vital parts is almost inevitable.

So far we have an A.C. voltage stepped down from house current and controllable up to 30 volts. But A.C. is useless for our little electric motors, electromagnetic and electroplating experiments. The current has to be made unidirectional, one wire always positive and the other negative. The device to accomplish this change is called a rectifier.

Not all rectifiers described in the textbooks meet our requirements, however. We are not concerned with elaborations like voltage stabilizers or even with a smoothed supply. A pulsating one will meet our needs just as well, and will moreover act as a charger for storage batteries.

We could broadly classify rectifiers as follows:

i. Large mercury-arc rectifiers for high power output.
ii. Rotary converter and vibrator-type rectifiers.
iii. Tube rectifiers.
iv. Electrolytic rectifiers.
v. Metal rectifiers.
vi. Crystal rectifiers, diodes, and transistors.

In our present consideration we omit *i* and *ii,* and *vi* is also eliminated on the score of very low power output although it is particularly suited to detection and the lower voltage requirements of radio circuits.

More precisely, then, what is meant by a rectifier? It is

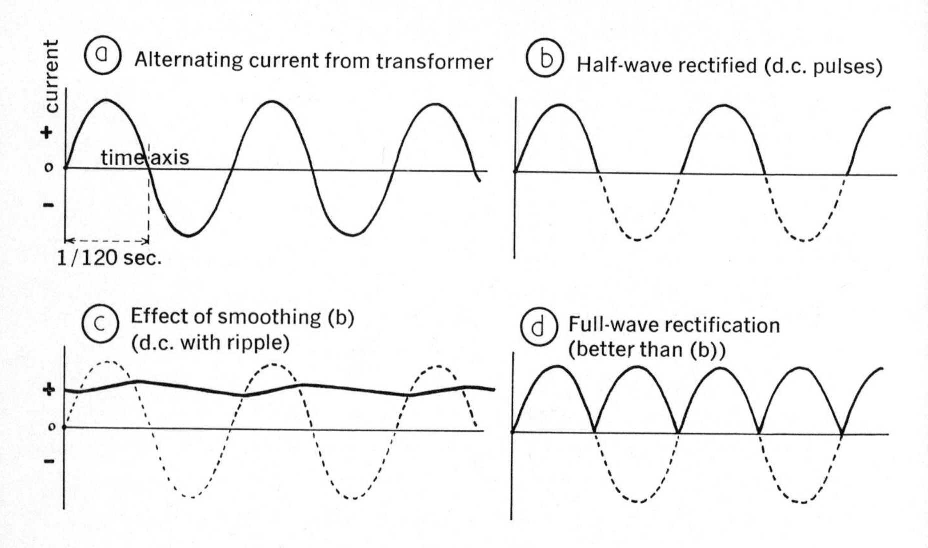

Fig. 59 Graphs of current before and after rectification

a device allowing current to flow readily in one direction while opposing with high resistance any flow in the reverse direction. In a sense, it behaves like a valve in a pipe which opens to flow of fluid in one direction and closes to the opposite flow.

In Fig. 59*a* we see the wave-form of 60 cycles per second A.C. voltage and current. Reversal of direction occurs after each $\frac{1}{120}$ second. The simplest rectifier cuts off the negative halves of the swings but passes on the positive halves, as in graph *b*. For the sake of readers perhaps familiar with the one-way action of a radio tube, we shall illustrate this process of half-wave rectification. The basic circuit is shown diagramatically in Fig. 60*a*, from which the heater supply to the tube filament has been omitted. It will be seen that the anode *A* of the tube is joined to S_1, one side of the transformer output coil supplying the A.C. When *A* swings positive, current flows across to the cathode *B*. (Note that the actual stream of electrons, negative particles, is in the reverse direction, from cathode to anode.) For the rest of the half-cycle, when *A* is negative, no current flows. Thus across points *DE* we could take off a pulsating D.C. supply such as is suggested by the solid line in the waveform (Fig. 59*b*). To obtain a steadier output current, two large storage capacitors, C_1 and C_2, are included, together with an inductance or choke *G* (Fig. 60*a*). This arrangement is known as smoothing the output. During the lost part of the wave the capacitors themselves are delivering power and the continuous line of Fig. 59*c* suggests the result.

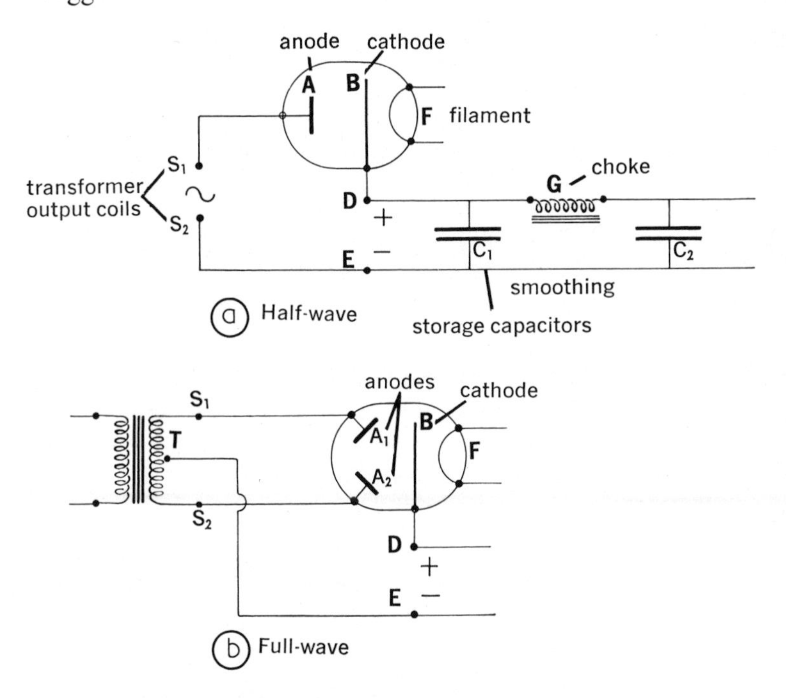

Fig. 60 Tube rectification

It is easily seen that we are here tapping only half of the available power supply by this process and a better circuit would employ both halves of the voltage swing. This is accomplished by using a center-tapped secondary winding on the transformer and more tubes. One common way of using current from each half-swing is to utilize a form of tube made with two anodes in it. Consider the anodes A_1 and A_2 shown in the diagram Fig. 60*b;* since one or other is always positive to the cathode *B,* the resulting current is much more continuous. Smoothing (not shown) is still required to eliminate the voltage ripple shown in Fig. 59*d,* where this is an undesirable feature. It would be added as already indicated in the half-wave unit.

An electrolytic rectifier, when constructed, will look like a large wet battery and have the disadvantage of containing dangerous acid. As such it must be housed and treated with due precautions.

Four jelly jars, Fig. 61*a,* should be lined with lead foil or with sheet lead *L,* obtained from a plumber. Support centrally in each jar a strip of tantalum metal foil *T* about 4 in. by ¼ in. For this purpose, blocks of insulator or cover plates of waxed wood *C* will have to be made for the jar tops. The tantalum itself is a somewhat expensive metal which will have to be bought from a chemical supply firm. It looks like springy steel and after some use has a blued appearance similar to that of a clock spring. The electrolyte in the cells *A* may be the ordinary sulphuric acid used in storage batteries of specific gravity about 1.2. The cells are joined in parallel; that is, all the center strips are linked together and form a small area electrode, while all the lead plates are connected together to form a large area electrode.

The group of rectifier cells, put in series with the 30-volt A.C. output from the transformer already described,

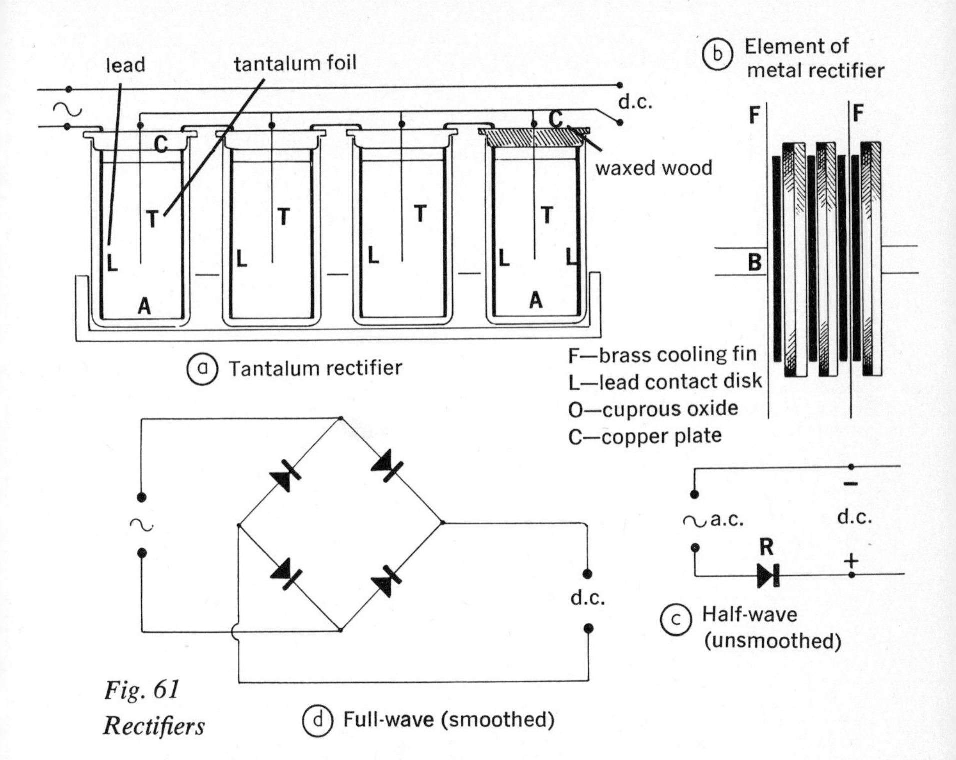

Fig. 61
Rectifiers

will then deliver a pulsating D.C. current. A big condenser, say 30 or 40 microfarads, across the output leads would largely smooth out the ripple as already explained.

The circuit diagram symbol for the rectifier is shown at *R* in Fig. 61*c*, and this represents the simplest use of the group of cells just mentioned. The cells are put in parallel as shown, in order to reduce the resistance and allow a current of several amperes to pass through. In the previous reference to diode valves as rectifiers, it should have been made clear that only a fraction of an ampere, perhaps up to ⅕, would flow, and also, in order to get a 350-volt output, a full-wave swing of 700 volts would be required from the input transformer. While this is the sort of D.C. supply often needed for radio work, it is not what is required for running models.

By far the most reliable and convenient device for our

purpose lies in class *v*, the copper oxide silenium or silicon type of rectifier. Unfortunately, this is not a component which the amateur can make and we can only suggest the purchase of such a unit from a radio-component dealer. Here one should not overlook the possibilities of Army-Navy surplus stores and the radio junk shops. The larger the component the better, as it will pass more current, and the higher voltage we intend to apply, the more plates will be needed.

This form of rectifier consists of a pile of plates bolted in close contact on an insulating rod. As shown in Fig. 61*b* the plates in each element are in sequence, brass cooling fin *F*, lead contact disk *L*, cuprous oxide facing *O*, bare copper side of plate *C*, lead disk, copper oxide and copper again, then lead, brass fin, and so on. To deal with house-current voltage there may be 20 or 30 sets of these elements in series. Wires are soldered onto the end cooling fins to serve as connectors for the unit. Current flows readily in the direction of the sequence stated above, but the resistance to flow in the opposite direction is very great. Since each oxide-copper element can stand up to 6 volts, a series of a dozen such elements should take a 30-volt peak voltage without breakdown.

Because of the superiority of full-wave over half-wave rectification, four of these units are commonly linked up in a group as shown in Fig. 61*d*. A little thought will show how this ingenious trick uses both halves of the voltage swing. Again, such a supply may require smoothing, as already explained, and input and output fuses are an obvious advantage, which should be allowed for in casing up the various components. In metering the output the voltmeter will naturally go across these terminals and the ammeter in series with them.

29 Simple Radio Receivers

When our radio set is unaccountably dead or inclines to the substitution of noisy crackles for music, a sharp blow with the fist is not always the best cure! On the other hand, casual delving beneath the outer panel of a modern radio set suggests to most people that rapid replacement of the panel is the wisest course. Indeed, the complicated maze of colored components and soldered circuitry is liable to shock the nonelectrically minded investigator. Repairs should be left to specialists. After over forty years of manufacturers' development and research, producing endless multielectrode tubes and best circuits, one nevertheless realizes that basic principles are still the same and that these can be grasped by the interested layman. The literature of radio is by now enormous, and in the space here available we cannot even define all the terms introduced. We must assume that the reader has some familiarity with common radio terminology.

Before we describe the simplest forms of radio sets it will be profitable to picture the events linking the broadcast and its reception. Radio waves are emitted, traveling with the same speed as light, from the transmitting aerial. They consist of a high- or radio-frequency carrier wave which, in the case of a 330-meter-wavelength broadcast, for example, would be at 908,000 cycles per second. This impressively high frequency is necessary if the waves are to carry big distances from the source. On the carrier wave, variations of amplitude are superimposed and this so-called modulation is at the much lower audio frequencies engendered by the actual music or other broadcast. Just as electromagnetic waves of light travel over immense distances, so do carrier waves reach very distant receivers.

If your aerial is to respond to the carrier wave it must have been accurately tuned to resonance with the particular frequency to be picked up. When so tuned, minute currents surge to and fro in the aerial system and it is the job of the receiver to adapt and magnify these ripples so that they are able to actuate telephone or speaker.

The tiny surges of current in the tuned aerial could not of course themselves affect headphones or speaker for at least two reasons. First, the frequency of the radio wave is so high that the diaphragm of the reproducer could not possibly respond to such a vast rate of vibration. Second, the currents fluctuate in direction and the individual wave energy is far too small to move the diaphragm.

The next step, then, is to rectify this incoming A.C. energy. By removing half of each cycle of the modulated carrier wave we convert the fluctuating energy of the radio waves into unidirectional pulses, and groups of such pulses provide enough energy to operate the phone unit. This is the work of some sort of detector or demodulator. An early device for this purpose was the crystal and cat's-whisker, though nowadays the same job is done by a crystal diode, a detector tube, or a transistor. The primitive detector was often a crystal of galena, bornite, molybdenite, or other metallic ore with a fine spring wire making light contact with some nicely selected spot. The selection of the best spot was a tricky business responsible for much childish heart-burning when careless heavy footfalls dislodged the whisker. The modern diodes are germanium crystals which have sealed contacts rendering them much more stable in operation.

Tuning the aerial to resonance is a matter of incorporating a coil of correct inductance and a condenser of correct capacitance. Alteration of either or both changes the natural frequency of the aerial-ground system. It is usually easiest to work with a fixed inductance, i.e., a permanent number of turns of wire, and alter only the capacitance by means of a variable condenser.

With this general picture in mind we now turn to our first efforts in making up a practical receiver. This is largely a matter of assembly and efficient layout. The components cannot for the most part be constructed but can easily be bought from radio dealers. A wealth of radio-set "junk" is available in suitable shops, and any number of scrapped sets, when dismembered, will provide sound, usable components for the builder. But beware of faulty items. Condensers obtained from cannibalized receivers should pass no direct current from a high-tension battery, and coils and transformers must be checked for continuity. Headphones and speakers also must be tested for continuity and produce suitable clicks on a D.C. source. Tubes and transistors require special test equipment not generally accessible, and discarded specimens are always suspect.

Simplest Crystal Set

Refer to Fig. 62*a* for the circuit diagram and collect the following components:

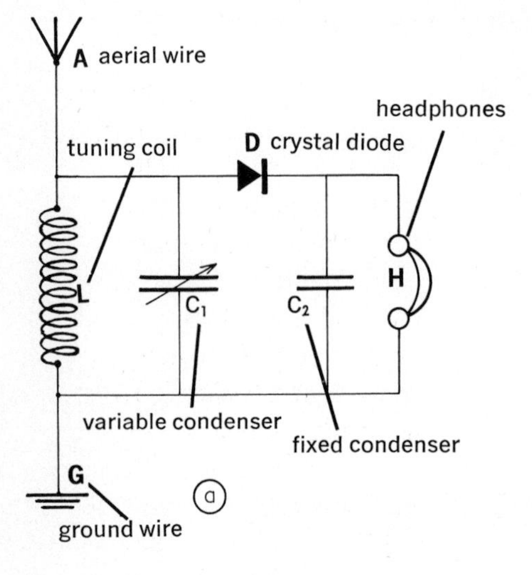

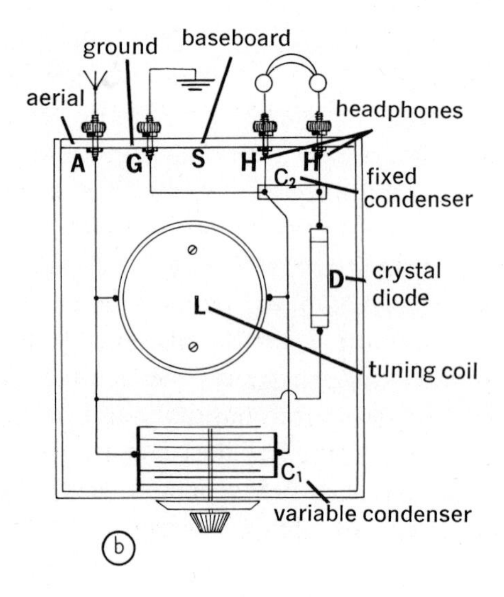

Fig. 62 Crystal receiver

1. The crystal diode *D*.
2. High-resistance headphones *H*, 2,000 or 4,000 ohms.
3. Variable condenser C_1, of capacity 0·0003 to 0·0005 μF.
4. Fixed condenser C_2, capacity 0·001 μF.
5. The tuning coil *L* (see below).
6. A high aerial wire, about 50 ft., on good insulators.
7. Ground wire to a waterpipe.
8. Terminals, tuning dial and knob, connecting wire.
9. Front panel and other casing material.

As regards the size of the case, the writer made one successful crystal set little larger than a matchbox, but a first attempt should be on a much bigger scale. While it is unnecessary to give dimensions to the set and its casing, as this will not materially influence its performance, in Fig. 62*b* the tuning coil *L* is a cylinder 2½ in. high cut from a plastic mug 2½ in. in diameter. This gives an idea of the scale of the box.

The actual box may be of plywood or aluminum sheet, but in any case components should be well insulated from it with bushings and washers. The tuning coil can be made very simply by carefully winding, in one layer, about 60 turns of either enameled magnet wire or D.C.C. copper wire, gauge 21. The spool for this may be a polyethylene beaker, a cut-down polyethylene bottle, or a cardboard tube. The turns should be neatly close-packed as winding proceeds, and if cardboard is used it should be insulated and hardened with a coat of shellac before and after winding the wire. The beginning and ending of the wire should be threaded through holes pricked in the tube, with several inches left for connection to other components. In this simple receiver the placing of the components is not at all critical as long as the insulation is perfect.

A strip of ebonite or polyethylene *S* is screwed across the rear of the baseboard to take four terminals marked *A* for aerial, *G* for ground, and *HH* for headphones, Fig. 62*b*. After a ⅜-in. hole is drilled through the center of the front panel the variable condenser C_1 is mounted behind it and the tuning dial and knob are fixed to the projecting spindle in front.

Wiring may be wholly joined to tightly screwed junctions (remember to put washers under nuts), but soldered connections are always preferable in radio work. Plastic sleeving slipped onto the bare copper connections makes for improved insulation and a workmanlike appearance. A good rule is to make wiring links as short as possible to avoid stray capacity effects. It is advisable to develop a good soldering technique from the start. Remember that certain components are easily ruined by even momentary accidental overheating. This especially applies to transistors, but the crystal diode used here is equally vulnerable. The advice to be followed is always to hold the pigtail wire in broad pliers between the component and the soldering point. Conduction by the cold pliers then acts as a heat sink, preventing heat from reaching the delicate crystal junction. Apply the same good habit when soldering resistors and capacitors, to avoid the annoyance of later breakdown. Multiflux-cored solder is very easy to use with an electric soldering iron provided the bit is cleanly tinned and the surfaces are also freshly scraped. A little practice may be necessary to produce neat junctions without an unpleasant superfluity of solder. The worst error, a dry joint, usually results from tarnished or greasy surfaces, wires that have been handled too much, or insufficient heat to make the solder flow properly.

Join A to the fixed plates of C_1 and the movable vanes to G. G also goes to a headphone terminal and to one side of the fixed condenser C_2. The other headphone terminal is joined to one side of the crystal diode and C_2, while the other side of the diode is fed from the aerial. A good ground is a large metal plate sunk in damp earth, but a cold-water pipe is also excellent. The wire to G may be heavy gauge and uninsulated.

If you are within a few miles of the transmitter the set may give good results with only an indoor aerial but otherwise a high outdoor aerial is advisable. This can be 50 ft. of stranded wire slung from large insulators and preferably well clear of the building. One advantage of the crystal set, a mixed blessing, is that it requires no batteries to energize it. Careful tuning should bring in several medium-wave stations at good headphone strength, but as the only source of energy is that picked up by the aerial, one cannot expect the power necessary to drive a loudspeaker. This requires amplification of the signal and a local source of battery power.

A Single-Tube Set

The chief difference between this set, shown in the circuit of Fig. 63*a,* and that of the previous model, lies in the replacement of the crystal rectifier by the vacuum tube V. This is a general-purpose vacuum tube known as a triode because of its anode, cathode, and grid. The filament forms the cathode of this simple vacuum tube and when hot it emits a stream of electrons (current in reverse direction) which are dragged across to the anode or plate. Particulars supplied with the vacuum tube give the correct high-tension battery voltage to be applied between the negative filament and the positive anode. The

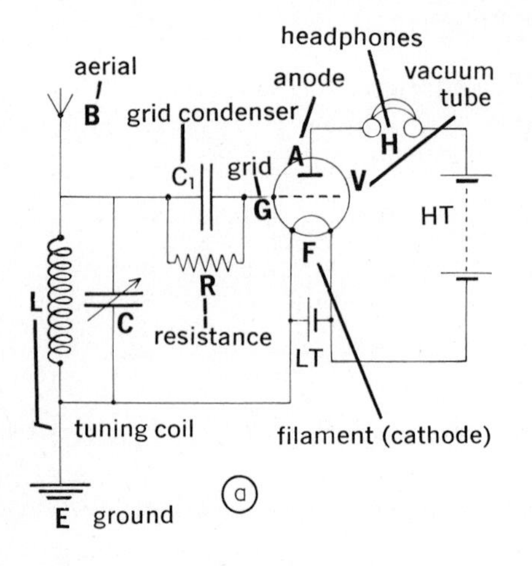

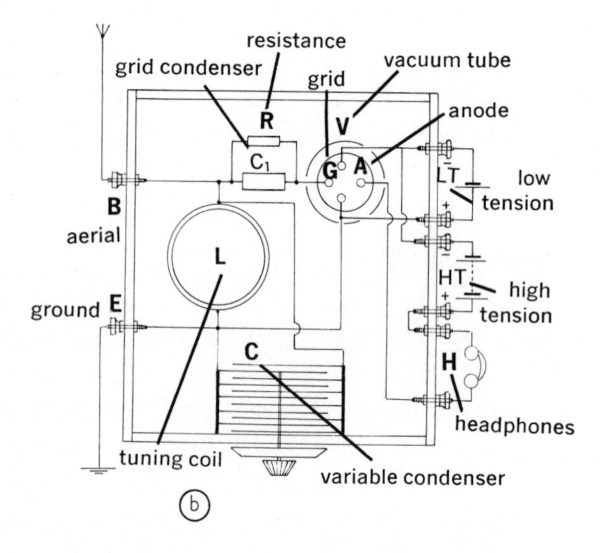

Fig. 63 Single tube receiver

makers also state whether the filament runs on 2 or 4 volts from a storage battery.

Compared with the previous circuit, the tuned aerial system is seen to be similar; not only does the vacuum tube rectify the input from this, but it also serves to amplify the signals. Instead of aerial-received energy it is in fact energy from the high-tension battery which drives the headphones. The hot cathode is responsible for the one-way traffic of electrons, i.e., the rectifying action. The grid is the key to the amplifying action. It is not difficult to see that the potential changes supplied to G by the aerial simply trigger the flow of current across the valve from A to F. G is much nearer the filament than A, and whenever G becomes negative the flow of electrons from F is reduced, but when it swings positive the flow is increased. Thus it is battery-supplied potential and current which fluctate in the headphone coils forming the anode load. This potential is a magnified replica of the pressure fluctuations on the grid, and these, of course, come from the aerial via the grid condenser C_1. The purpose of the high resistance R is to avoid accumulation of charge on the grid, as this can now leak through R and L to ground.

A somewhat larger container may be needed for this set in order to accommodate the vacuum tube, but a 6-in.-sq. base and a 4-in. height should be adequate. Additional requirements are:

1. General-purpose vacuum tube V.
2. Low-tension storage battery (2-volt or value applicable to V).
3. High-tension battery (60-volt or value applicable to V).
4. 4-pin vacuum-tube holder.

5. Grid condenser C_1 (0·0001 μF).
6. Grid leak R (2 megohm).
7. 8 terminals altogether, now including two for low tension and two for high tension.

The tuning dial is mounted on the front panel as before (see Fig. 63*b*) and insulated terminal strips are screwed to the left and right sides of the box. Always keep the aerial leads well away from the high tension and make the connection to the valve grid as short as possible. Precautions to be observed in building a tube set concern the fragile nature of the filament. This is easily destroyed by jarring or burning out through applying more than the correct voltage. Therefore label the low- and high-tension terminals very clearly and take great care not to let the high tension reach the filament by any momentary mis-connection.

Unfortunately, the set described has very obvious limitations. The simple tuning coil limits the choice of stations to medium waves. The selectivity is poor and the power output, even using a high aerial, is small. But if you are interested in building good sets there are many developments possible. Find out from radio books how to wind other coils; long-wave coils can be added and then shorted-out by a switch when using the medium waves. Huge increase of power and of selectivity is possible in regenerative receivers. In these, a little of the local battery power feeds back energy, through a reaction coil coupled with the tuning coil, into the aerial inductance. Plenty of speaker power is also given by a multi-stage vacuum tube amplification and by push-pull output systems. Then there are considerable advantages in using the superheterodyne principle, in which the receiver generates a frequency of its own, but these are matters which require special study by the young radio technician.

A Crystal Set with Amplification by One Transistor

We have seen comparable circuits employing first a crystal diode and then a vacuum tube for the combined purpose of rectification and amplification. We shall now consider how a transistor also can do the work of amplification. There are certain advantages in this little device which is so rapidly becoming ubiquitous in electronics. Transistors are minute compared with vacuum tubes and are robust to handle. They are cheap and with a vast market they ought to become still cheaper. The power they consume is negligibly small and its source, one or two dry cells, lasts for months.

Fig. 64 gives details of the present design. Since the transistor itself is such a tiny unit we may go further in exploiting compactness and reduce dimensions all around. Instead of the old-fashioned air-spaced condenser we shall fit a small solid dielectric variable 0·0005 μF. Instead of the open inductance we may wind a compact little coil on a ferrite rod about 2 in. long and at the same time allow a winding for the long-wave reception. In this elementary design we shall have to use a good outside aerial, but in multitransistor sets with powerful amplification the ferrite rod itself makes an adequate aerial. The extras now needed are:

1. A 0·01 μF fixed condenser.
2. About 2 in. of ferrite rod.
3. About 10 yd. enameled wire A.W.G. 28 to 31.

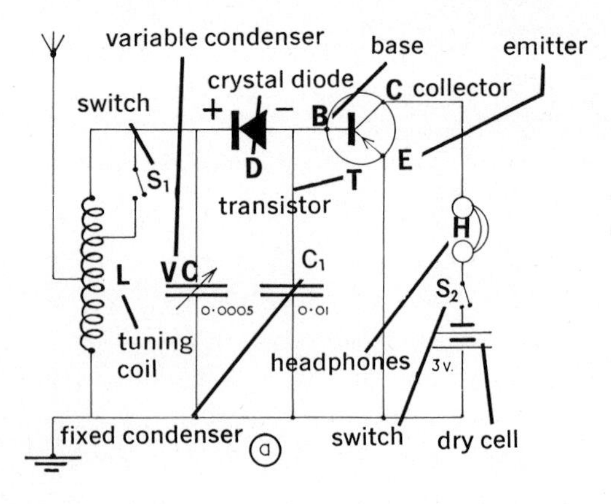

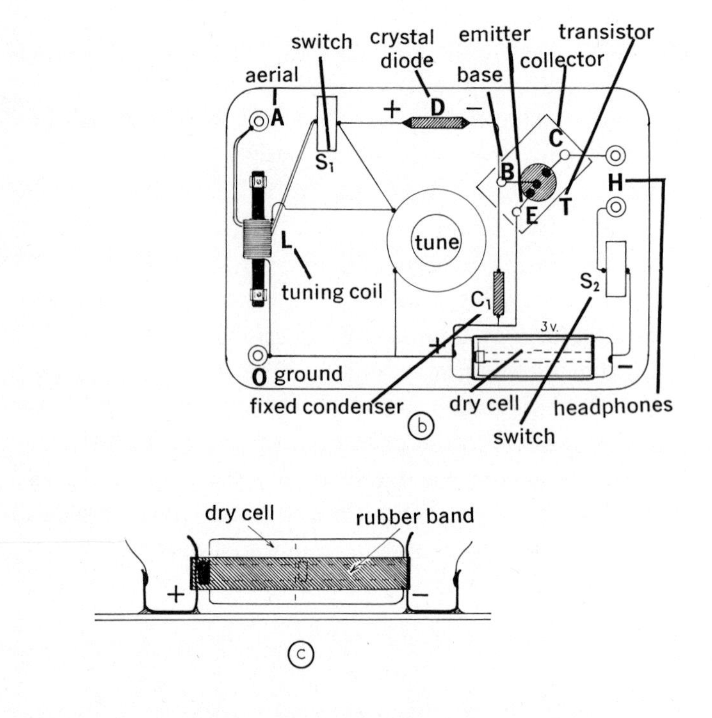

Fig. 64   Diode and transistor receiver

4. An audio-type transistor.
5. An on-off switch.
6. A 3-volt dry cell.
7. Connecting wire and sundry screws and washers.

For mounting the components we require insulated panels, and it is suggested that a plastic food box giving a base area about 7 in. by 4½ in. and 1½ in. deep is ready-made and ideal for the purpose. The material of transparent plastic boxes is very brittle and likely to crack on being drilled. It has therefore been found advisable to melt through the holes for the condenser spindle and terminals by means of a well-heated metal rod of suitable size. Resulting thickening at the edges of the holes adds strength, but where necessary the surplus may be removed with a sharp knife. Terminal tag strips can always be added inside the box. By mounting these on wooden blocks, glued on with epoxy, one may avoid screws through the outer case. Good insulating panel and terminal strips could be made from scraps of Lucite or Formica, and a discarded plastic dishpan could be a good source of polyethylene. The tuning condenser, knob, and dial may be central on the base of the inverted box, but positioning of the components depends on whether it is intended that a little speaker be added later, and may be left to the discretion of the builder.

The tuning coils are wrapped on a piece of special iron core called ferrite rod, which may be as short as 1½ in. First, insulate ½ in. of the middle of the rod with a wrapping of cellophane tape. Using the fine-gauge wire, wind 20 turns and tap out a loop 3 or 4 in. long. Proceed to wrap on another 40 turns, tap out as before, smooth over with cellophane tape, and finally wind on another 140 turns. The winding should be overlaid on the central

½ in. and held in place with a binding of adhesive tape. Of course, 3 or 4 in. of wire are left for connections at the beginning and end of the full coil, and the enamel is scraped off these ends and the twisted tapping loops. The first 60 turns, forming the medium-wave coil, are joined to the aerial by the first tap; see *L* in Fig. 64*b*. The on-off switch S_1 merely shorts-out the 140 turns when the medium waves are being tuned, and when the switch is open the complete set of turns is in use as a long-wave coil.

The ferrite rod and also the battery may be held in adjustable hose clamps of suitable size. Otherwise the 3-volt dry cell requires a simply made holder. Cut two tag strips ½ in. wide by 2 in. long from a tin box and bend them as shown in the thick line of Fig. 64*c*. Solder 4-in. wires to each tin strip and glue these tags beneath the top panel with epoxy, leaving a gap just the length of the battery. A strong rubber band around these two tags and the battery makes an effective holder with good contacts. Actually, the battery is not fitted until all the wiring has been completed and thoroughly checked.

In our first crystal set the polarity of the crystal was immaterial, but in this case it does matter: The diode must be correctly connected with its negative side toward the transistor, as shown at *D*.

As to the audio transistor itself, this is called a *PNP*-type. It has three leads to its germanium crystal. A large contact area on one crystal face is known as the base *B*. A positive point contact *E* is the emitter and this takes in the signal. The neighboring collector contact *C* is maintained negative and supplies the amplified image. *C* is usually marked with a red spot and *B* is always the middle wire, so no confusion should arise. This is vitally important, as the transistor would be destroyed if wrongly connected or if the battery was inserted the wrong way around. Mark the positive battery-holder tag with a dab of red nail polish and remember that the central rod (carbon) of the dry cell goes to the red side when inserting a new battery. The base, collector, and emitter are clearly shown in Figs. 64*a* and *b*. It is probably best for the beginner to leave the three transistor-wire tails their original length, and use screws for linkage rather than solder, thereby avoiding any possibility of heat-damage.

If desired, the second switch S_2 may be omitted, since the action of plugging in the headphones connects up the negative side of the battery to the collector and while the headphones are disconnected the cell is not being wasted. It should have a life of some months, according to the amount of use, since the current drain is only in the region of a milliampere. Do not try to improve the output of the set by increasing the battery voltage beyond 4·5 volts or you may ruin the transistor.

To obtain optimum results from a radio set like this may involve some experimentation with the number of turns on the aerial coil, since the best number is dependent on the particular piece of ferrite used, the external aerial attached, and other factors. Reasonable volume of reproduction in headphones should in any case be obtainable.

In conclusion, it must be appreciated that the three sets described have been chosen to illustrate the basic principles of radio reception rather than for efficiency, and it is hoped that the functions of the components have been clarified. Making these sets must be regarded as only a first step in radio, perhaps whetting the appetite of newcomers to this fascinating branch of electronics. The scope of the tiny transistors is rapidly widening and future physicists should learn about their astonishing capabilities. Perhaps the building of a really good-quality multi-transistor set will be the reader's next goal.

Index